First published in 2000
This edition published in 2002 by
Miles Kelly Publishing Ltd
Bardfield Centre, Great Bardfield, Essex, CM7 4SL

2 4 6 8 10 9 7 5 3 1

Questions written by Clive Gifford
Cartoons by Mark Davis
Cover artwork by Mike Roberts

Design: Jo Brewer
Page Make-up: Helen Weller
Proof reader: Lynn Bresler
Production: Estela Godoy
Editorial Assistants: Janice Bracken & Kirsty Allen

Art Director: Clare Sleven
Editorial Director: Paula Borton

British Library Cataloguing-in-Publication Data
A catalogue record for this book is available from the British Library

ISBN 1-84236-151-1

Printed in Hong Kong

Contents

General Knowledge

Here are 37 quizzes to test your general knowledge.
You will find questions here on all the other categories in
Quiz Time. It's a real pot luck section that will see how much
you know about everything from science, animals and famous
people to computers, painters and the solar system.

The questions are divided into three levels of difficulty:
Easy Peasy, Clever Clogs and Whiz Kids. As you can probably
guess Easy Peasy are the easiest, Clever Clogs the next most
difficult and Whiz Kids the hardest. However, the easiest
questions are always the ones where you know the answers!

Good luck.

Quiz 1

1. What alcoholic drink is made from crushed grapes?

2. What is the name for the stick carried by a British policeman or woman?

3. What transport machine has forks, gears and a chainwheel?

4. What stately home in Britain is famous for its maze?

5. Who is the cartoon and comic strip sailor who loves spinach?

6. What is a male elephant called?

7. How many letters are there in the alphabet?

8. Is a great bustard an old-fashioned gun, a bird or a type of drink?

9. What are a sombrero and a deerstalker examples of?

10. In which city would you find the shop Harrods?

LOOK DAD, I ROLLED IT ALL BACK UP FOR YOU!!

Answers

Quiz 2

Clever Clogs

1 Who was the captain of the England rugby team in the 1999 World Cup?

2 An American quarter is worth how many cents?

3 What is the Japanese art of Bonsai?

4 In which country was a wok originally used for cooking?

5 Which chain of stores use the brand name *St Michael*?

6 What sort of food is a courgette?

7 What colour are taxis in New York?

8 What part of a bishop's clothing is his mitre?

9 Are all metals magnetic?

10 When were the Olympics last held in Britain?

Answers

1. Martin Johnson 2. 25 3. Growing miniature tree 4. China 5. Marks and Spencer 6. A vegetable 7. Yellow 8. His hat 9. No 10. 1948

Quiz 3

Whiz Kids

1 An American dime is worth how many cents?

2 Which record company announced a merger with Time-Warner in 2000?

3 Who was captain of the England cricket team before Nasser Hussein?

4 Ash Wednesday is the first day of which religious period?

5 Which is the most easterly country: Norway, Sweden or Finland?

6 Who wrote the play *Troilus and Cressida*?

7 What do we call the time that a baby spends inside its mother's womb?

8 Who was selected as Labour Party candidate for Mayor of London in 2000?

9 If you were born on April 5, what star sign would you be?

10 On what part of the body do cowboys wear chaps?

Answers

1. Ten 2. EMI 3. Alec Stewart 4. Lent 5. Norway 6. Shakespeare 7. Gestation period or pregnancy 8. Frank Dobson 9. Aries 10. Legs

Quiz 4

1 How many weeks are there in a year?

2 Red sky at night is whose delight?

3 From which country does lasagne and spaghetti come?

4 Where are coffins buried?

5 What relation is Prince Charles to Prince Philip?

6 How many tens are there in a thousand?

7 How many television channels for all viewers does the BBC fund?

8 What part of the coffee plant is harvested to make the drink?

9 Which buildings have blue lamps outside them in Britain?

10 Which is longer a foot or a yard?

Answers

1. 52 2. Shepherds' 3. Italy 4. In a graveyard 5. Son 6. 100 7. Two 8. The beans 9. Police stations 10. A yard

Clever Clogs

1 What was the first name of the composer Beethoven?

2 Which charity runs Red Nose Day?

3 With what sport is Nick Skelton associated?

4 What sort of creature is a tarantula?

5 Who plays the lead in *The Vicar of Dibley*?

6 What is the fastest airliner in the world?

7 What car-maker's previous models include the Capri and the Anglia?

8 What street features the prime minister's official London residence?

9 In which country is the world's longest wall?

10 How many English kings have been named Edward?

Answers

1. Ludwig 2. Comic Relief 3. Horse-jumping 4. A spider 5. Dawn French 6. Concorde 7. Ford 8. Downing Street 9. China 10. Eight

Quiz 6

1 What is measured in firkins?

2 Which band played a New Year's Eve night concert at Cardiff's Millennium Stadium?

3 Whose assembly line revolutionized car-making in the early 20th century?

4 What is the connection between *Wayne's World* and *Austin Powers: International Man of Mystery*?

5 How many make up a score?

6 Who was the most famous marshall of the wild west town of Tombstone?

7 What is the name for the regular rise and fall of the sea?

8 Which athletics commentator hosted *A Question of Sport* before Sue Barker?

9 What year did the great storm cause much damage and destroy many trees in southern England?

10 How many birth signs are there in the Zodiac?

Answers

1. Liquid 2. Manic Street Preachers 3. Henry Ford 4. Mike Myers wrote and starred in both of them 5. Twenty 6. Wyatt Earp 7. Tide 8. David Coleman 9. 1987 10. Twelve

Quiz 7

1 How many lungs does the human body contain?

2 What phone number is usually dialled for the emergency services in Britain?

3 What are the three emergency services?

4 In cockney rhyming slang, what does "apples and pears" mean?

5 Where would you find woofers and tweeters?

6 If you were born on March 7, what would your star sign be?

7 Can you give the first name of Victoria and David Beckham's son?

8 What are Danish blue, Brie and Gouda examples of?

9 What colour was the Beatles' submarine?

10 Which soap has a pub called the *Rovers Return*?

Answers

1. Two 2. 999 3. Police, Fire and Ambulance 4. Stairs 5. Loudspeakers 6. Pisces 7. Brooklyn 8. Cheeses 9. Yellow 10. *Coronation Street*

Quiz 8

1 In which city would you find Madison Square Gardens?

2 Which airline sponsored the London Eye ride in London?

3 Was the Spanish Main in the Caribbean, Red or Mediterranean Sea?

4 How many make up a baker's dozen?

5 Who wore togas?

6 Which British city sits on the River Lagan?

7 What is 1 and $^3/_5$ in decimal numbers?

8 Who led the knights of the round table?

9 What tree gives its name to the syrup poured over pancakes?

10 In which TV soap did Dirty Den, Arthur Fowler and Angie once appear?

Answers

1. New York 2. British Airways 3. Caribbean 4. 13 5. Romans 6. Belfast 7. 1.6 8. King Arthur 9. Maple 10. EastEnders

1 What does a numismatist study?

2 Which player aimed a kung-fu kick at a Crystal Palace supporter and was banned?

3 Who is the quiz master on *Countdown*?

4 What is the first letter of the Greek alphabet?

5 What vegetable is sauerkraut made from?

6 What does simultaneously mean?

7 What is the square root of 121?

8 In which city were houses first given numbers?

9 Which language is described as Hispanic?

10 Which European city is famous for its Oktoberfest?

Answers

Quiz 10

1. Which precious stone is red?

2. Pikachu is a character in which cartoon series?

3. How many five pences in a pound?

4. What is a winklepicker: a bird, a type of hunting knife or a shoe?

5. If you were using split shot on a line tied with a size 16 hook, what would you be doing?

6. Is a minidisk: a way of storing computer information or music?

7. Name the board game that you would be playing if you landed on Mayfair?

8. What is the ninth letter of the alphabet?

9. How many sevens are there in 35?

10. How many sides does a dice have?

Answers

1. The ruby 2. Pokémon 3. Twenty 4. A shoe 5. Fishing (angling) 6. Music 7. Monopoly 8. I 9. Five 10. Six

Quiz 11

Clever Clogs

1. In cockney rhyming slang, what is a "trouble and strife"?

2. What are granny, reef and sheepshank examples of?

3. What boyband did Robbie Williams used to be in?

4. Where would you be most likely to find an alternator?

5. What was the name of the sheep in *Wallace and Gromit*?

6. Lord Baden Powell founded which movement?

7. In the Bible, how many apostles did Jesus have?

8. An early version of what machine was called a "boneshaker"?

9. What substance makes bread rise?

10. With what sort of drink is the campaign group CAMRA associated?

Answers

1. A wife 2. Knots 3. Take That 4. In a car engine 5. Shaun 6. Scouts 7. Twelve 8. Bicycle 9. Yeast 10. Real ale (beer)

Quiz 12

1 According to the old phrase, what did curiosity do to the cat?

2 What daytime quiz show does Carol Vorderman star in?

3 If you were born on December 27, what would your star sign be?

4 If you were performing a cascade or shower, what pastime would you be taking part in?

5 What name did the ancient Greeks give to a supposed large island west of Gibraltar?

6 What number does the Roman numeral M equal?

7 What is the last letter of the Greek alphabet?

8 What is mulligatawny?

9 In which film did Tommy Lee Jones and Will Smith fight aliens?

10 Chelsea, Spode and Royal Doulton are types of what?

Answers

1. Kill it 2. *Countdown* 3. Capricorn 4. Juggling 5. Atlantis 6. 1,000 7. Omega 8. A soup 9. *Men in Black* 10. Porcelain

Quiz 13

Easy Peasy

1 What is 1.25 as a fraction?

2 What is the key ingredient of an omelette?

3 Which boyband includes lead singer Ronan Keating?

4 What is the national airline of Canada?

5 Used in World War II, what sort of device were U-boats?

6 With what films do you associate Darth Maul and Darth Vader?

7 What does the French word "Bonjour" mean?

8 How many days in the month of April?

9 Would you fish with, eat or kick a melon ball?

10 How many 10 pence pieces are there in twenty pounds?

Answers

1. 1¼. 2. Eggs 3. Boyzone 4. Air Canada 5. Submarines 6. *Star Wars* 7. Hello or Good Day 8. 30 9. Eat it 10. 200

Quiz 14

1   Is oxtail soup really made from ox's tail?

2   What is the real-life name of the lady who plays Pauline Fowler in *EastEnders*?

3   Which country was once ruled by tsars?

4   What does the French word "oeuf" mean in English?

5   Which Michael Jackson video was the most expensive ever made?

6   In cockney rhyming slang, what is a "frog and toad"?

7   Which was the first Boeing jet airliner?

8   How old is a centenarian?

9   Was Westlife, Point Break or Boyzone number one in the 1999 Christmas charts?

10   If you were at a bureau de change what would you be doing?

Answers

1. Yes 2. Wendy Richards 3. Russia 4. Egg 5. *Thriller* 6. Road 7. Boeing 707 8. 100 9. Westlife 10. Changing money into a different currency

QUIZ 15

1. Who wrote tales about Flopsy, Mopsy and Cottontail?

2. What is a chow?

3. Which national radio station does Chris Evans present on?

4. What word means a type of pig meat and an amateur radio operator?

5. What building traditionally has three balls displayed outside?

6. Who had a hit with *No Scrubs* in 1999?

7. What is the national airline of Indonesia?

8. Was the Battle of Inkerman in the Crimean, Boer or Falklands War?

9. In which city did Anne Frank live?

10. In which month does the grouse shooting season start in Britain?

Answers

1. Beatrix Potter 2. A breed of dog 3. Virgin Radio 4. Ham 5. A pawnbrokers 6. TLC 7. Garuda 8. Crimean 9. Amsterdam 10. August

Quiz 16

Easy Peasy

1 What does the Roman numeral V equal?

2 Which is the higher belt in Judo: black or yellow?

3 Beetle, Golf and Polo are all made by which motor manufacturer?

4 How many hours in two days?

5 In what structure would Clark Kent visit to change into Superman?

6 How many years have a couple been married if they're celebrating their silver wedding?

7 What colour is the gemstone ruby?

8 Which popular author is the sister of actress Joan Collins?

9 Emulsion and enamel are types of what?

10 How many eighths are there in a half?

Answers

1. Five 2. Black 3. Volkswagen (VW) 4. 48 5. A telephone box or booth 6. 25 7. Red 8. Jackie Collins 9. Paint 10. Four

Quiz 17

1 According to folklore, what does the sandman help children to do?

2 Who hosted the TV show *Blind Date*?

3 Which Greek philosopher was made to commit suicide by drinking hemlock?

4 What does the phrase "Parlez vous Anglais" mean in English?

5 In which European country is the port of Antwerp?

6 Which TV show has been hosted by Johnny Vaughan, Mark Little, Peter Kay and Chris Evans?

7 Which English king was killed at the Battle of Bosworth in 1485?

8 What can be divided into stanzas: time, food or poetry?

9 The moons Oberon and Miranda orbit which planet?

10 Which language was invented to be a universal language?

Answers

1. Go to sleep 2. Cilla Black 3. Socrates 4. Do you speak English 5. Belgium 6. *The Big Breakfast* 7. Richard III 8. Poetry 9. Uranus 10. Esperanto

Quiz 18

Whiz Kids

1 What do the initials AWOL stand for in the military?

2 What year in the 20th century was the bikini invented?

3 What unusual pet did the Roman, Julius Caesar, have?

4 Nick Park is behind which popular animated characters made of modelling clay?

5 Is Ezra a book of the Old or New Testament?

6 The astrological sign Cancer is shown as what type of creature?

7 What day of the week does the German word Dienstag refer to?

8 Who is the lead singer of the Manic Street Preachers?

9 In which country is Vesuvius found?

10 What word means to "invent" and "cosmetics"?

Answers

1. Absent With Out Leave 2. 1946 3. Giraffe 4. Wallace and Gromit 5. Old Testament 6. A crab 7. Tuesday 8. James Dean Bradfield 9. Italy 10. Make up

Quiz 19

1 What word, beginning with K, is the correct term for tomato sauce?

2 What device currently orbiting Earth was named after the astronomer Edwin Hubble?

3 Are Airbus aircraft made by a group of American, European or Asian companies?

4 Did Alex Ferguson become manager of Manchester United in 1986, 1993 or 1996?

5 St Clare is the patron saint of television – true or false?

6 What is 0.75 as a fraction?

7 What are bourbon, digestive and malted milk examples of?

8 What colour has shades known as scarlet and vermilion?

9 How many threes are there in 63?

10 In paints, what two colours do you mix together to get green?

Answers

10. Blue and yellow

1. Ketchup 2. The Hubble Space Telescope 3. European 4. 1986 5. True 6. ³/₄ 7. Biscuits 8. Red 9. 21

Quiz 20

1 Is a sole a freshwater or saltwater fish?

2 How many years have a couple been married if they are celebrating their golden wedding?

3 Which Spice Girl sang on a hit single with Bryan Adams?

4 In the nursery rhyme, which town was Dr Foster heading to: Towcester, Gloucester or Worcester?

5 What trade did Jesus learn?

6 If you were born in February, what gem would be your birthstone?

7 What sort of clothing item is a homburg?

8 Which cartoon pirate has an enemy called Black Jake?

9 In French it is "jeudi", in German it is "Donnerstag"; what day of the week is it in English?

10 In imperial measurements, how many pints equal a UK gallon?

Answers

1. Saltwater 2. 50 3. Mel C 4. Gloucester 5. Carpentry 6. Amethyst 7. A hat 8. Captain Pugwash 9. Thursday 10. Eight

1 On what date did the Chinese New Year of 2000 fall?

2 What number do people dial in the United States to get their emergency services?

3 In Roman numerals, what number is represented by CXXXVII?

4 What TV show launched the career of actor/singer Will Smith?

5 What British building traditionally has a red and white striped pole displayed outside?

6 Who is the quiz master on *University Challenge*?

7 Where is the Prime Meridian situated?

8 The *Niña*, the *Pinta* and the *Santa Maria* were the three ships in the voyage commanded by what famous explorer?

9 What is the main vegetable ingredient of the Russian soup, borscht?

10 Where would you find derailleur gears?

Answers

Quiz 22

Easy Peasy

1 What sort of animal was often killed by a harpoon?

2 What do the initials NHS stand for?

3 Is A6 paper bigger than A5?

4 Which science fiction film starred Ewan McGregor as a Jedi Knight?

5 What is a museum of the stars called?

6 What sort of animal is a pug?

7 In a pack of cards, does the queen of clubs look to her left or right?

8 How can you tell that a car has a learner driver in it?

9 What colour is the bird, the canary?

10 If you walk up something do you ascend or descend?

Answers

1. A whale 2. National Health Service 3. No, it is half the size of A5 4. *Star Wars Episode i: The Phantom Menace* 5. Planetarium 6. A dog 7. Left 8. By the L-plate sign displayed on the car 9. Yellow 10. Ascend

Clever Clogs

1 How many years have a couple been married if they are celebrating their diamond wedding?

2 Which female singer was with the Fugees before having solo success?

3 In Roman numerals, what number is represented by CXIII?

4 What are the first names of the two Geordie lads who host *SMTV* on Saturday mornings?

5 What was the stage name of the pair when they were a singing duo?

6 If you were born in January, what gem would be your birthstone?

7 Is the currency of China: the Yuan, the Yen or the Yinni?

8 How many people usually make up a jury in England and Wales?

9 What kind of food comes from Bakewell?

10 What word is both a harbour and a socket on the back of a personal computer?

Answers

1. 60 2. Lauryn Hill 3. 113 4. Ant and Dec 5. PJ and Duncan 6. Garnet 7. Yuan 8. 12 9. A tart 10. Port

Quiz 24

Whiz Kids

1 According to Chinese tradition, is the year 2000 the year of the cat, the monkey or the dragon?

2 If you were born on the October 1, what star sign would you be?

3 In Roman numerals, what number is represented by XIX?

4 Which TV soap did singer Adam Ricketts used to star in?

5 In which English county would you find Matlock?

6 What date is St Stephen's feast day?

7 In computing, what does USB stand for?

8 What is the currency of Pakistan?

9 In which Dutch city does the International Court of Justice sit?

10 The Asian country of Cambodia was formerly known as what?

Answers

1. Year of the dragon 2. Libra 3. 19 4. *Coronation Street* 5. Derbyshire 6. December 26 7. Universal Serial Bus 8. Rupee 9. The Hague 10. Kampuchea

Quiz 25

1 What year was the last ever Five Nations rugby union tournament played?

2 What are the two red suits in a pack of cards?

3 What fruit, beginning with A, is shaped like a small peach?

4 Which tennis tournament is famous for strawberries and cream and its Centre Court?

5 Does the word "amplify" mean to make sound louder or quieter?

6 What British mammal lives in a sett and has a distinctive black and white striped head?

7 If you "bottle up" your feelings, what do you do with them?

8 Is the first book of the Bible, Exodus, Genesis or Psalms?

9 How many edge sides does a 50 pence piece have?

10 What is the past tense of the word drink?

Answers

1. 1999 2. Hearts and diamonds 3. Apricot 4. Wimbledon 5. Louder 6. Badger 7. Keep them to yourself 8. Genesis 9. Seven 10. Drank

31

Quiz 26

Clever Clogs

1 What does "in the buff" mean?

2 What animal represents the star sign Taurus?

3 Which ex-American president was nicknamed "Tricky Dicky"?

4 In the nursery rhyme, what could Jack Sprat's wife not eat?

5 Who wrote and directed the *Star Wars* films?

6 What sort of aircraft were the Lancaster and the Stirling?

7 What instrument are Gibson, Les Paul and Fender famous for making?

8 What flavour is the drink crème de menthe?

9 Chiropody is the treatment of what part of your body?

10 What is the square root of 64?

Answers

1. Naked 2. A bull 3. Richard Nixon 4. Fat 5. George Lucas 6. Bombers (from World War II) 7. Electric guitars 8. Mint 9. Your feet 10. Eight

QUIZ 27

1 If you had MP3 files running through a player, what would you be doing?

2 What is the more commonly used name for the musical instrument, the timpani?

3 What is the chemical symbol for chlorine?

4 What word, beginning with H, means New Year's Eve in Scotland?

5 What is the highest female voice?

6 How many revolutions per minute did an old-fashioned LP used to turn at?

7 St Bona is the patron saint of air hostesses – true or false?

8 What name is given to a creature which lives on another animal and gets its food from it?

9 The World War II Battle of the Leyte Gulf was between Japan and which other country?

10 "Slick Willie" is the nickname of which United States president?

Answers

1. Listening to music downloaded form the Internet 2. Kettle drum 3. Cl 4. Hogmanay 5. Soprano 6. 33 and 1/3 rpm 7. True 8. Parasite 9. The United States 10. Bill Clinton

Quiz 28

Easy Peasy

1 Who sells houses and other properties?

2 Around what part of your body might you wear a dicky bow?

3 What is the opposite of temporary: infinite, enormous or permanent?

4 Were tea bags invented in the 1420s, the 1620s or the 1920s?

5 Which country does Liebfraumilch wine come from?

6 Are the Prodigy a dance music act, a comedy sketch team or an American basketball team?

7 What relation is the brother of your father to you?

8 Which national side has Colin Hendry played football for?

9 What are the largest of all plants: seaweed, trees or cacti?

10 Where would you find a meteorite: underwater, in a desert or in space?

Answers

7. Your uncle 8. Scotland 9. Trees 10. In space

1. An estate agent 2. Your neck 3. Permanent 4. 1920s 5. Germany 6. A dance music act

Quiz 29

1 Is a cor anglais a woodwind, stringed or percussion instrument?

2 What name is given to a small round beetle with black spots on its red wings?

3 What are you if you are laid-back?

4 What sort of drink is Adam's ale?

5 What is the largest stringed instrument?

6 What subject is the quiz show *They Think It's All Over* about?

7 Is the tale of Daniel and the lions in the Old or New Testament of the Bible?

8 What creature represents the star sign, Capricorn?

9 How old do you have to be to hold a full driving licence in Britain?

10 Where is the sting of a scorpion situated?

Answers

1. Woodwind 2. Ladybird 3. Relaxed 4. Water 5. Harp 6. Sport 7. Old Testament 8. A goat 9. 17 10. In its tail!

Quiz 30

1 In Greek mythology, who was set twelve labours?

2 In Roman numerals, what number is represented by XXXIX?

3 What word, beginning with F, means accidental success?

4 Which country did Albert Einstein become a citizen of in 1901?

5 Is a leveret a young rabbit, hare or ferret?

6 What is the largest brass instrument?

7 Juno and Gold Beaches were landing points for which World War II invasion?

8 How many American senators are elected from each US state?

9 Name the first of the Wallace and Gromit films?

10 Is the Sun a thousand, a million or 100 million times bigger than Earth?

Answers

1. Hercules 2. 39 3. Fluke 4. Switzerland 5. A young hare 6. The tuba 7. D-Day (Normandy landings) 8. Two 9. A Grand Day Out 10. A million

Quiz 31

1　How many sides has a 20 pence piece?

2　If you fixed water pipes in a house, what would your job title be?

3　Poodles were once used as hunting dogs — true or false?

4　Who were the first people to live in New Zealand: the Maoris, the Aborigines or the Spanish?

5　How do Americans spell grey?

6　How many strings does a violin have?

7　What two paint colours would you mix to make purple?

8　If you serve a double fault, what sport are you playing?

9　What word means a small downpour of rain and also a bathroom spraying device?

10　In which continent is the country Togo situated?

Answers

1. Seven 2. A plumber 3. True 4. Maoris 5. Gray 6. Four 7. Red and blue 8. Tennis 9. Shower 10. Africa

Quiz 32

1 Who, in the Bible, was swallowed alive by a whale?

2 Does the musical term adagio mean fast, bass or very slow?

3 If you were born in April, what gem would be your birthstone?

4 What is the name of a building used to store aircraft?

5 What do the initials VAT stand for?

6 What creature would you be eating if you were served calimari?

7 What food, made from a stuffed sheep's stomach, is often eaten on Burn's Night?

8 What does the word "utterly" mean?

9 What day of the week is called "Mittwoch" in German?

10 If you are wily, are you: tall and thin, rude or cunning?

Answers

1. Jonah 2. Very slow 3. Diamond 4. Hangar 5. Value Added Tax 6. Squid 7. Haggis 8. Completely 9. Wednesday 10. Cunning

Quiz 33

Whiz Kids

1 Is contralto the highest or lowest female voice?

2 What Moroccan port gives its name to the fruit, the tangerine?

3 What subject is the quiz show *Never Mind the Buzzcocks* about?

4 Riga is the capital of Latvia, Lithuania or Estonia?

5 The TV show *Stars in Their Eyes* is hosted by which Kelly: Lorraine, Gene or Matthew?

6 If you were born in May, what gem would be your birthstone?

7 Sir Alf Ramsey managed which English sports team in the 1960s?

8 Nassau is the capital of Bermuda, the Bahamas or Trinidad and Tobago?

9 If you were born on June 18, what would be your star sign?

10 If you cook something in a case of pastry, would your dish be: en croute, al fresco or pot au feu?

Answers

1. The lowest 2. Tangiers 3. Pop music 4. Latvia 5. Matthew Kelly 6. Emerald 7. Football team 8. The Bahamas 9. Gemini 10. En croute

Quiz 34

1 Does the rice dish risotto come from India, Wales or Italy?

2 Which Sheriff was an enemy of Robin Hood?

3 What type of appliance is the name Dyson associated with?

4 Who was born Elizabeth Alexandra Mary of Windsor?

5 Were the Velvet Underground a pop music band, a terrorist group or a group of modern artists?

6 What body part are biceps and triceps?

7 What is 0.5 of 11?

8 What is someone who sells fruit and vegetables called?

9 What foodstuff can come in UHT, condensed and semi-skimmed?

10 What is 20% of 200?

OOH DEAR!

Answers

1. Italy 2. Sheriff of Nottingham 3. Vacuum cleaner 4. Queen Elizabeth II 5. A pop music band 6. Muscles 7. 5.5 8. A greengrocer 9. Milk 10. 40

Clever Clogs

1 According to the grammatical rule, what letter comes before e except after c?

2 If you cook food slowly in a covered pan are you braising it, flash-frying it or blanching it?

3 In the Vietnam War, did the United States join the side of the South or North Vietnam forces?

4 David Trimble is a politician in which part of the United Kingdom?

5 What nationality was the composer Richard Wagner?

6 Was Caligula: a Viking warlord, a Saxon king or a Roman emperor?

7 Is hypothermia when your body gets very hot, very cold or lacking water?

8 Which melon has pink flesh and lots of large black seeds?

9 What is the world's most popular sport?

10 What name is given to a fertile place in a desert?

Answers

7. Very cold 8. Watermelon 9. Football 10. Oasis

1. I 2. Braising 3. South Vietnam 4. Ulster (Northern Ireland) 5. German 6. Roman emperor

Quiz 36

1 Anne of Burgundy was the first woman to receive what sign of an impending marriage?

2 How old was Sir Stanley Matthews when he stopped playing professional football?

3 How old was he when he died in February 2000?

4 What was the last record the Beatles made: *Sgt Pepper's Lonely Hearts Club Band*, *Abbey Road* or *Let It Be*?

5 What name is given to a law judge's small wooden hammer?

6 What London Underground line is coloured brown on a map?

7 In what year did Margaret Thatcher become British prime minister?

8 Was she the first ever female prime minister?

9 What are progeny: fragments of Moon rock, a class of virus or children?

10 What's the official language of Haiti?

Answers

1. A diamond engagement ring 2. 50 3. 85 4. *Let It Be* 5. A gavel 6. Bakerloo 7. 1979 8. Yes 9. Children 10. French

Quiz 37

1 In which James Bond film did the character of Oddjob appear?

2 What is the name of the headquarters of the Metropolitan Police Force?

3 Which fish makes spectacular leaps upstream to return to its birthplace?

4 Who was the first Frenchman to manage Arsenal football club?

5 What are the horns of a stag called?

6 If someone is Oxbridge-educated, which university other than Oxford may they have attended?

7 What are *Pravda*, the *Washington Post* and the *Miami Herald*?

8 In which athletics event did Steve Backley once hold the world record?

9 Which European country has the continent's only active volcanoes?

10 What garden creature, beginning with F, starts life as a tadpole?

Answers

7. Newspapers 8. The javelin 9. Italy 10. Frog

1. *Goldfinger* 2. New Scotland Yard 3. The salmon 4. Arsene Wenger 5. Antlers 6. Cambridge

English

Here are 37 quizzes to test your knowledge of English.
They include questions on English language, books, writers
and so on.

The quizzes are divided into three levels of difficulty:
Easy Peasy, Clever Clogs and Whiz Kids. As you can probably
guess Easy Peasy are the easiest, Clever Clogs the next most
difficult and Whiz Kids the hardest. However, the easiest
questions are always the ones where you know the answers!

Good luck.

Easy Peasy

1　What word is a type of fish and means the bottom of a shoe?

2　What was the name of the house where Toad lived?

3　Who wrote *Macbeth* and *Twelfth Night*?

4　What kind of animal was Barbar?

5　What do sentences always start with?

6　Who was Romeo in love with?

7　What do the initials RIP stand for?

8　What sort of words are run, jump, talk and fall?

9　What is the name of the punctuation symbol used to provide a pause in a sentence?

10　What is the word fridge short for?

Quiz 2

1 How many thieves were with Ali Baba?

2 What word is a flat-bottomed boat and a long kick of a football or rugby ball?

3 What is the meaning of the phrase "to keep your nose clean"?

4 In the nursery rhyme, what did the cow jump over?

5 Which is the first book of the Bible?

6 Who marched his men up to the top of the hill?

7 What letter can you add to ham to make a word meaning false, fake or fictitious?

8 Who wrote the James Bond books?

9 What sort of animal was Tarka?

10 What is the plural of the word goose?

Answers

1. 40 2. Punt 3. To stay out of trouble 4. The Moon 5. Genesis 6. The Grand Old Duke of York 7. S (sham) 8. Ian Fleming 9. An otter 10. Geese

Quiz 3

Whiz Kids

1. Which famous poet recently re-wrote the ancient tale of *Beowulf*?

2. What word can mean to knock and a sort of container?

3. Who or what is shanks's pony?

4. What brothers were famous for writing fables and tales?

5. What is a cat o' nine tails?

6. What word is a part of an elephant and the body of a tree?

7. Who wrote *A Brief History of Time*?

8. What special feature do words or phrases which are palindromes have?

9. What title did Sir John Betjeman hold for many years?

10. What does YMCA stand for?

Answers

1. Seamus Heaney 2. Jar 3. To walk on foot 4. The Brothers Grimm 5. A form of whip 6. Trunk 7. Stephen Hawking 8. They read the same forwards and backwards 9. Poet Laureate 10. Young Men's Christian Association

47

Quiz 4

1. What building holds books for public use?

2. Which doctor is famous for *Green Eggs and Ham* and other silly stories?

3. If schoolchildren play truant, what do they do?

4. Which bird is often given the nickname Polly?

5. What is the name of the dog in the *Peanuts* stories?

6. What type of animal is featured in *Watership Down*?

7. What word do Americans use to describe the boot of a car?

8. What job does Pat do in the books written by John Cunliffe?

9. What does the phrase "to lose your marbles" mean?

10. What sort of book contains the spellings of words?

Answers

1. A library 2. Dr Seuss 3. Stay off school 4. A parrot 5. Snoopy 6. Rabbits 7. Trunk 8. He is a postman 9. To go mad 10. A dictionary

Quiz 5

1 Who wrote the book *Animal Farm*?

2 What word is an alcoholic drink, a little like sherry, and a sort of harbour?

3 What do the initials NUS stand for?

4 Which nursery rhyme character was eating curds and whey?

5 What is the past tense of steal?

6 What is the plural of wolf?

7 Is the phrase A Santa at Nasa a palindrome?

8 Who was in wonderland and went through the looking-glass?

9 What do the initials NFA stand for?

10 What book featured a man-child called Mowgli?

Answers

1. George Orwell 2. Port 3. National Union of Students 4. Miss Muffet 5. Stole 6. Wolves 7. Yes 8. Alice 9. No Fixed Abode 10. *The Jungle Book*

Quiz 6

Whiz Kids

1 What word means a book written by a person about their life?

2 What does the Latin phrase bona fide mean?

3 Who is the child star of the books written by J.K. Rowling?

4 What grammatical term is "Super Sam Smashes Sampras" an example of?

5 What do the initials ESP stand for?

6 In *Tom's Midnight Garden*, who was Tom's friend from another age?

7 What word means a group of seals or whales?

8 How many *Hitch-Hiker's Guide to the Galaxy* books are there?

9 Which comedian co-wrote the *Blackadder* scripts with Richard Curtis?

10 What word can be added to pet to mean a floor covering?

Answers

1. Autobiography 2. In good faith 3. Harry Potter 4. Alliteration 5. Extra-Sensory Perception 6. Hattie 7. A pod 8. Four 9. Ben Elton 10. Car

Quiz 7

1 What group of animals are called a pride?

2 Which children's book asked the reader to search for a character with a shortened version of the name Walter?

3 Who had a teddy bear, nicknamed Winnie the Pooh?

4 What sort of stories are associated with the writer Hans Christian Andersen?

5 What do you do if you "chance your arm"?

6 In the nursery rhyme, what were Jack and Jill going up the hill to get?

7 What does the abbreviation HMS stand for?

8 What town is closely associated with Shakespeare?

9 What type of creature were Tomsk, Orinocho and Bungo?

10 What do the initials WWF stand for?

Answers

1. Lions 2. *Where's Wally?* 3. Christopher Robin 4. Fairy tales 5. Take a risk 6. A pail of water 7. His, or Her, Majesty's Ship 8. Stratford-upon-Avon 9. Wombles 10. World Wrestling Federation

Quiz 8

Clever Clogs

1. Who is the world's most successful horror writer with books including *Misery*, *Rose Madder* and *The Shining*?

2. What was the name of Winnie the Pooh's small, pink friend?

3. What word can mean to hobble and is used to describe something that is floppy?

4. In the Alice stories, what creature could be found asleep in a teapot?

5. Is a coracle: a prophet, a council meeting place or a boat?

6. What word is a boy's name, a duck's beak and a note of the cost of something?

7. In the nursery rhyme, what was the King doing in his counting house?

8. Which early reading books feature Pat the dog?

9. Who wrote *Sons and Lovers*?

10. In *Treasure Island*, who was Captain Flint?

Answers

1. Stephen King 2. Piglet 3. Limp 4. A dormouse 5. A boat 6. Bill 7. Counting out his money 8. Peter and Jane 9. D.H. Lawrence 10. A parrot

Quiz 9

Whiz Kids

1　Which poet wrote *The Waste Land*?

2　What short word can you place after feather, flower and sick?

3　What word is used to describe a group of crows?

4　What does the abbreviation NSPCC stand for?

5　Who wrote the long-running play *The Mousetrap*?

6　Who wrote *The Silmarillion* and *The Hobbit*?

7　Which trilogy of books is the above author most renowned for?

8　What was the name of the dog in *Peter Pan*?

9　Who wrote the *Little House on the Prairie* stories?

10　In what books would you find George and Timmy?

Answers

1. T.S. Elliot 2. Bed 3. A murder 4. National Society for the Prevention of Cruelty to Children
5. Agatha Christie 6. J.R.R. Tolkein 7. *The Lord of the Rings* 8. Nana 9. Laura Ingalls Wilder
10. *The Famous Five*

Quiz 10

1 Who did Fagin and the Artful Dodger take under their wing?

2 What do the initials UN stand for?

3 What subject has Delia Smith written many successful books about?

4 R.L. Stein writes what sort of book?

5 What does the phrase "last gasp" mean?

6 What do the initials RSPB stand for?

7 What do the letters o.g. stand for in football?

8 What would you call a group of birds?

9 In the nursery rhyme, how many birds were baked in a pie?

10 Which famous book character was described as "a bear of very little brain"?

Answers

1. Oliver Twist 2. United Nations 3. Cookery 4. Horror books for children and teenagers
5. Right at the end or the last moment 6. Royal Society for the Protection of Birds 7. Own goal
8. A flock 9. 24 10. Winnie the Pooh

Quiz 11

1 What sort of words are adjectives?

2 What do the initials TUC stand for?

3 Which famous author wrote *Bleak House*?

4 In which city was Shakespeare's Globe Theatre?

5 What book gives lists of words with similar meanings?

6 What name is found on the most common version of the above?

7 What does the abbreviation WWW stand for?

8 Which Brontë wrote *Wuthering Heights*?

9 What letter can be added to the word loop to make the name of a type of ship?

10 Which pop star's frank autobiography was called *Is That It*?

Answers

1. Words that describe something 2. Trades Union Congress 3. Charles Dickens 4. London
5. A thesaurus 6. Roget's 7. World Wide Web 8. Emily 9. S (sloop) 10. Bob Geldof

Quiz 12

1 What word means to have loaned someone something and is also a religious date on the calendar?

2 Which early reading books featured a boy and a girl both with names starting with the letter J?

3 Is a braggart: a boastful person, a part of a horse or a petty criminal such as a thief?

4 What is an antonym?

5 Can you give an antonym of miserly?

6 What is an antonym of risky?

7 Which author of over 500 romantic stories claimed to write each book in just seven days?

8 Which female author wrote the book on which the film *The Color Purple* was based?

9 With what sort of books was Wainwright associated?

10 Who wrote *The Canterbury Tales*?

I'M SLOW TODAY, I'VE ONLY WRITTEN 50,000 WORDS.

SCRIBBLE SCRIBBLE

Answers

1. Lent 2. *Janet and John* 3. A boastful person 4. A word which means the opposite of another word 5. Generous 6. Safe 7. Barbara Cartland 8. Alice Walker 9. Walking guides 10. Chaucer

Quiz 13

Easy Peasy

1 Which children's book character has a friend called Big Ears?

2 Where did Little Jack Horner sit?

3 What letter can be added to the word hop to mean a store?

4 What letter is usually followed by u in English words?

5 Which creature finally eats Captain Hook?

6 What letter can be added to hat to mean talk?

7 What animal is the book *Black Beauty* about?

8 Which boy wizard has stormed to fame in a series of books?

9 What are the five vowels?

10 Who wrote the *Famous Five* books?

Answers

1. Noddy 2. In the corner 3. S (shop) 4. Q 5. A crocodile 6. C (chat) 7. A horse 8. Harry Potter 9. A E I O U 10. Enid Blyton

57

Quiz 14

1 What kind of creature was Bilbo Baggins?

2 Which fictional detective had an enemy called Moriarty?

3 Which famous detective's first appearance was in the book *The Mysterious Affair at Styles*?

4 What do the initials QC mean in law?

5 Who wrote tales about Brer Rabbit?

6 What two words, which sound the same but are spelt differently, mean certain and a beach?

7 Who is the boy who never grew up?

8 Who's World War II diaries portrayed the horrors of religious persecution?

9 Who wrote the book *The Iron Man*?

10 In what horror story does Jonathan Harker hunt down a vampire?

Answers

1. A hobbit 2. Sherlock Holmes 3. Hercule Poirot 4. Queen's Counsel 5. Uncle Remus 6. Sure and shore 7. Peter Pan 8. Anne Frank 9. Ted Hughes 10. *Dracula*

Quiz 15

1 Who wrote the horror story *The Pit and the Pendulum*?

2 In which series of books would you find Ford Prefect and Arthur Dent?

3 Who wrote nonsense verse including the poem *The Owl and the Pussycat*?

4 What is a synonym?

5 Can you give a synonym of the word cheerful?

6 What is a synonym of the word gigantic?

7 Which English romantic poet wrote *To Autumn*, *Ode to a Nightingale* and *To Hope*?

8 Which famous sleuth played the violin and wore a deerstalker hat?

9 What would you be if you were accused of having "short arms and deep pockets"?

10 Which famous writer has published books such as *The Running Man* under the pseudonym Richard Bachman?

Answers

1. Edgar Allen Poe 2. *The Hitch-Hiker's Guide to the Galaxy* 3. Edward Lear 4. A word which means the same as another word 5. Happy 6. Huge, enormous 7. John Keats 8. Sherlock Holmes 9. Mean or miserly 10. Stephen King

Quiz 16

Easy Peasy

1 Which Norse god gave his name to Thursday?

2 What do the initials PTO stand for?

3 What is the name of the first Harry Potter book?

4 What is the name of Harry's unusual school?

5 Who visits a chocolate factory in the Roald Dahl story?

6 Which fantasy author has written *Mort*, *Truckers* and *Dangerous Creatures*?

7 How many people speak in a monologue?

8 How does one feel if they are "tickled pink"?

9 Which Charles wrote *Great Expectations*?

10 What type of animal is Spot?

Answers

1. Thor 2. Please turn over 3. *Harry Potter and the Sorcerer's Stone* 4. Hogwarts 5. Charlie 6. Terry Pratchett 7. One 8. Happy, delighted 9. Charles Dickens 10. A dog

Quiz 17

1 Who wrote *Oliver Twist*?

2 What word is given to the letters of the alphabet which are not vowels?

3 Did George Orwell or George Elliot write *The Road to Wigan Pier*?

4 Which satirical magazine was started by Peter Cook and is edited by Ian Hislop?

5 Which famous lady detective was the star of a number of books written by Agatha Christie?

6 Who wrote the adventure story *Kidnapped*?

7 What term is used to describe a number of kangaroos?

8 What is the name of the system of organising books found in most libraries?

9 What newspaper was nicknamed The Thunderer?

10 Which comedian wrote *Stark* and *Popcorn*?

Answers

1. Charles Dickens 2. Consonants 3. George Orwell 4. *Private Eye* 5. Miss Marple 6. Robert Louis Stevenson 7. A troop 8. The Dewey Decimal System 9. *The Times* 10. Ben Elton

Quiz 18

1 What is the removable paper cover on many hardback books called?

2 Which comedian wrote *The Liar* and *Hippopotamus*?

3 Which word means to illustrate and to tie in a contest?

4 Past, future, and present are examples of what section of grammar?

5 What is a pseudonym?

6 Which ex-Goon has written comic versions of *Black Beauty* and *Dracula*?

7 What was the title of Sir Alex Ferguson's best-selling autobiography?

8 How many does the prefix deci- signify?

9 Which mystery writer's books include *Death in the Air*, *The ABC Murders* and *Evil Under the Sun*?

10 What annual prize for adult novels was won in 1999/2000 by an adaptation of *Beowulf*?

Answers

1. Dust jacket 2. Stephen Fry 3. Draw 4. Tenses 5. A false name used by a writer 6. Spike Milligan 7. *Managing My Life* 8. Ten 9. Agatha Christie 10. The Whitbread Prize

Quiz 19

1 What is the plural of the word sheep?

2 In the nursery rhyme, did Jack or Jill fall down the hill last?

3 What bear came from Peru and is incredibly fond of marmalade?

4 What word, meaning halt, rhymes with hop?

5 What vegetable turned into a carriage for Cinderella?

6 At what time did the carriage turn back into the vegetable?

7 Is a minuet: a gun, a dance or a type of castle tower?

8 On which London common do the Wombles live?

9 Of which country is Robert Burns the national poet?

10 In the nursery rhyme, which old woman went to fetch her dog a bone?

Answers

9. Scotland 10. Old Mother Hubbard

1. Sheep 2. Jill 3. Paddington 4. Stop 5. A pumpkin 6. Midnight 7. A dance 8. Wimbledon

Quiz 20

1 What word is used to describe a group of hens?

2 Which book about four sisters was written by Louisa May Alcott?

3 What word describes a person turning pink with embarrassment?

4 Who wrote the book *Frankenstein*?

5 Which famous poet was the author of Frankenstein married to?

6 Which great detective's last case was described in the book *Curtains*?

7 Which famous writer had her book *Pride and Prejudice*, rejected by a number of publishers?

8 What word is used to describe a group of dancers?

9 What book about a young lord was written by Frances Hodgson Burnett?

10 Which female author wrote *Malory Towers*, *The Secret Island* and the *St Clare's Naughtiest Girl* series?

MMM...
I LOVE BOOKS...

..ESPECIALLY WITH SALT ADDED.

Answers

1. A brood 2. *Little Women* 3. Blush 4. Mary Shelley 5. Percy Shelley 6. Hercule Poirot 7. Jane Austen 8. A troupe 9. *Little Lord Fauntleroy* 10. Enid Blyton

Quiz 21

1 What is the surname of Harry Potter's horrid Aunt and Uncle?

2 Which prolific author is in the *Guinness Book of Records* for writing 26 books in one year, 1983?

3 Which David wrote the award-winning *Skellig* and *Kit's Wilderness* novels for children?

4 What is a curmudgeon?

5 Which detective had a close friend called Captain Hastings?

6 Which writer and wit said "I have nothing to declare but my genius"?

7 Which female writer, who died in 1817, wrote *Northanger Abbey* and *Mansfield Park*?

8 Where did the Pied Piper come from?

9 Which fairy tale character had long golden hair?

10 According to the old saying, what does "absence make"?

Answers

1. Dursley 2. Barbara Cartland 3. David Almond 4. A bad-tempered person 5. Hercule Poirot 6. Oscar Wilde 7. Jane Austen 8. Hamelin 9. Rapunzel 10. The heart grow fonder

Quiz 22

1 What was the title of the second of the Harry Potter books?

2 Which ex-goon wrote *Adolf Hitler: My Part in his Downfall* and *Milliganimals*?

3 What would you be if you were described as "long in the tooth"?

4 For what sort of books is Mrs Beeton best known?

5 What word can mean a schoolchild and part of the eye?

6 In the old rhyme, who killed Cock Robin?

7 What is the opposite of the word patient?

8 Who was Sherlock Holmes' faithful assistant?

9 What is the past tense of the word creep?

10 What do the initials MP stand for?

Answers

1. *Harry Potter and the Chamber of Secrets* 2. Spike Milligan 3. Old 4. Cookery 5. Pupil 6. The sparrow 7. Impatient 8. Doctor Watson 9. Crept 10. Member of Parliament and Military Police

Quiz 23

1   Which writer and playwright wrote *The Importance of Being Earnest* and *The Ballad of Reading Gaol*?

2   Which Harriet wrote *Uncle Tom's Cabin*?

3   Whose first novel was *Carrie*, published in 1974?

4   Who wrote *Sophie's World*?

5   Which Brontë wrote *Jane Eyre*: Charlotte, Emily or Anne?

6   What word, meaning a bad smell, rhymes with pink?

7   Who wrote about the BFG (Big Friendly Giant)?

8   What do the initials ASAP stand for?

9   What word can mean an aircraft and a woodworking tool?

10 What word is used to describe a group of ants?

Answers

1. Oscar Wilde 2. Harriet Beecher Stowe 3. Stephen King 4. Jostein Gaarder 5. Charlotte 6. Stink
7. Roald Dahl 8. As Soon As Possible 9. Plane 10. A colony

Quiz 24

1 Which writer wrote *The Secret Garden*?

2 Who writes fantasy novels about Discworld?

3 Who wrote *The Origin of the Species*?

4 What was the book about?

5 When you add -ly to an adjective what type of word do you normally create?

6 In Greek mythology, which character's weak point was his heel?

7 Who wrote *The Cider House Rules* and *The World According to Garp*?

8 What is the meaning of the word turmoil?

9 Which member of the Royal family wrote *The Old Man of Lochnagar* in 1980?

10 Which Shakespearean character was known as the Prince of Denmark: Othello, Hamlet or King Lear?

Answers

1. Frances Hodgson Burnett 2. Terry Pratchett 3. Charles Darwin 4. The theory of evolution 5. An adverb 6. Achilles 7. John Irving 8. A state of great confusion or unrest 9. Prince Charles 10. Hamlet

Quiz 25

1 How many ugly sisters did Cinderella have?

2 What is the name of the little yellow bird in the *Peanuts* books?

3 What do the initials MW stand for on a radio?

4 Which book character "robbed from the rich and gave to the poor"?

5 Did he live in Epping Forest, Sherwood Forest or the New Forest?

6 What is the past tense of the word eat?

7 Who went to London to seek his fortune and eventually became Mayor?

8 Which postman has a black and white cat?

9 Can you complete the book title, *The Lion, The Witch...*?

10 What is the name of the Bogeyman in the Raymond Briggs book?

MORNING...

Answers

1. Two 2. Woodstock 3. Medium Wave 4. Robin Hood 5. Sherwood Forest 6. Ate 7. Dick Whittington 8. Postman Pat 9. *and The Wardrobe* 10. Fungus

Quiz 26

Clever Clogs

1 Who wrote the Sherlock Holmes mysteries?

2 Which ancient Greek character fell in love with himself?

3 Who wrote the books on which the *Jaws* films were based?

4 In which books would you find a character called Obelisk?

5 Who writes and draws the *Kipper* stories?

6 Who wrote *The Snowman* and *Father Christmas*?

7 Who wrote *The Hitch-Hiker's Guide to the Galaxy*?

8 Who wrote *Kubla Khan* and *The Rime of the Ancient Mariner*?

9 What animals star in the book *Ring of Bright Water*?

10 Who wrote *Emma* and *Sense and Sensibility*?

Answers

1. Sir Arthur Conan Doyle 2. Narcissus 3. Robert Benchley 4. The Asterix books 5. Mick Inkpen 6. Raymond Briggs 7. Douglas Adams 8. Samuel Taylor Coleridge 9. Otters 10. Jane Austen

1   Americans call them restrooms; what do British people call this room?

2   Which sci-fi author wrote a number of books about robots, including *I, Robot*?

3   What mystical land did C.S. Lewis write about?

4   What are you doing if you "burn the candle at both ends"?

5   Complete the title of the Shakespeare play *Two Gentlemen of...*?

6   What are you doing if you are "bending over backwards"?

7   Who wrote *Kim* and the *Just-So* stories?

8   What word do Americans use instead of undertakers?

9   What is a scene if it is picturesque?

10 In which story would you find Gandalf the wizard and Smaug the dragon?

Answers

1. Toilets or washrooms 2. Isaac Asimov 3. Narnia 4. Working too hard 5. *Verona* 6. Trying very hard 7. **Rudyard Kipling** 8. Morticians 9. Attractive and interesting 10. *The Hobbit*

Quiz 28

1 Complete the proverb "A stitch in time..."?

2 Which boy's secret diaries were first written when he was aged 13 ³/₄?

3 Whose travels did Jonathan Swift write about?

4 What land of tiny people was the character in the above book shipwrecked on?

5 What bird does the Ugly Duckling turn into?

6 What is the term sci-fi short for?

7 Complete the proverb "Many hands make..."?

8 What type of animal was Winnie the Pooh's bouncy friend called Tigger?

9 What type of animal is Bagheera, a character in *The Jungle Book*?

10 Who did Dr Jekyll turn into when he drank the potion he had developed?

Answers

1. Saves nine 2. Adrian Mole 3. *Gulliver's Travels* 4. Lilliput 5. A swan 6. Science fiction 7. Light work 8. A tiger 9. A black panther 10. Mr Hyde

Quiz 29

1 Which book about a horse did Anna Sewell write?

2 Who wrote *My Family and Other Animals*?

3 On which Greek island was most of the book set?

4 Which Arsenal supporter wrote *Fever Pitch* and *About a Boy*?

5 Which Doctor encountered a Push Me-Pull You in his travels?

6 Which Tess did Thomas Hardy write about?

7 Which Australian author wrote *Misery Guts* and *Water Wings*?

8 Who wrote the *Animal Ark* series of books?

9 Who wrote *The French Lieutenant's Woman*, *The Magus* and *The Collector*?

10 Which Shakespeare play features the characters Viola, Malvolio and Sir Toby Belch?

Answers

1. Black Beauty 2. Gerald Durrell 3. Corfu 4. Nick Hornby 5. Doctor Doolittle 6. Tess of the d'Urbervilles 7. Morris Gleitzman 8. Lucy Daniels 9. John Fowles 10. *Twelfth Night*

Quiz 30

1 Is a barnacle: a shellfish, a type of oar or an ancient weapon?

2 Which fairy tale character sold his family's cow for a handful of beans?

3 Who wrote the original Dr Jekyll story?

4 What do you intend doing if you want to "turn over a new leaf"?

5 Which sci-fi author wrote *Rendezvous With Rama*, *The Sands of Mars* and *Childhood's End*?

6 If you are asked to "shake a leg", what should you do?

7 Who wrote *Lord of the Flies*?

8 What Shakespeare play title is considered bad luck for actors to mention?

9 Which author wrote *The Crow Road* and *The Wasp Factory*?

10 What initial does he add to his name when writing sci-fi stories?

Answers

1. A shellfish 2. Jack from *Jack and the Beanstalk* 3. Robert Louis Stevenson 4. Start afresh 5. Arthur C. Clarke 6. Hurry up 7. William Golding 8. *Macbeth* 9. Iain Banks 10. M. (Iain M. Banks)

Quiz 31

Easy Peasy

1 Did Arthur Miller or Arthur Ransome write *Swallows and Amazons*?

2 What do the initials CD stand for?

3 In which books would you find Captain Haddock and a dog called Snowy?

4 In which books would you find Linus, Lucy and Peppermint Patty?

5 Complete the title of the Shakespeare play, *The Taming of...*?

6 How many days did it take for Phileas Fogg to travel around the Earth?

7 How many people would you find in a duet?

8 According to the proverb, what do "too many cooks" do?

9 What word, starting with f, do Americans use for the Autumn season?

10 In which tales would you find Friar Tuck and Maid Marian?

Answers

1. Arthur Ransome 2. Compact Disc 3. *Tin-Tin* 4. *Peanuts* 5. *The Taming of the Shrew* 6. 80 days 7. Two 8. Spoil the broth 9. Fall 10. *Robin Hood*

Quiz 32

Clever Clogs

1   Who wrote the Adrian Mole books?

2   Who was Adrian Mole's girlfriend?

3   Who wrote *Robinson Crusoe*?

4   Which Thomas wrote *The Mayor of Casterbridge* and *Jude the Obscure*?

5   Complete the title of the Shakespeare play *A Midsummer...*?

6   Does a prologue start or end a story?

7   What would be your alma mater?

8   Who wrote *The Time Machine* and *War of the Worlds*?

9   What word means both attractive and quite?

10   How many people would you find in a quintet?

Answers

QUIZ 33

1 *Prince Caspian* and *The Voyage of the Dawn Treader* are part of which *Chronicles*?

2 What would you be if you were a "stick in the mud"?

3 What golden prize were Jason and the Argonauts seeking out?

4 Is the Jason and the Argonauts story a part of ancient Greek, Roman or Viking mythology?

5 What do Americans call spanners?

6 Who wrote *2001: A Space Odyssey* and had a TV series about the *Mysterious World*?

7 In which book does Wendy Darling and the "lost boys" appear?

8 Which Sir Walter wrote romantic adventures including *Ivanhoe* and *Waverley*?

9 Can you complete the book title *The Last of the...*?

10 What do the initials RAC stand for?

Answers

1. *The Narnia Chronicles* 2. Resistant to change 3. The golden fleece 4. Ancient Greek 5. Wrenches 6. Arthur C. Clarke 7. *Peter Pan* 8. Sir Walter Scott 9. *Mohicans* 10. Royal Automobile Club

Quiz 34

1   In which pantomime does Widow Twankey appear?

2   What handy aid to spelling was first compiled by Dr Samuel Johnson?

3   What is the meaning of the initials UFO?

4   Who was the one-legged pirate in the adventure story *Treasure Island*?

5   What word is a common writing instrument and a fenced in area to hold sheep?

6   What American word is used to mean a lift?

7   What would you do if you "spilled the beans"?

8   What letter would you add to rain to mean a railway vehicle?

9   Complete the title of the Shakespeare play *Antony and…*?

10 What is the name of the lion in the Narnia books: Alvera, Leo, Aslan or Larry?

Answers

1. Aladdin 2. Dictionary of English 3. Unidentified Flying Object 4. Long John Silver 5. Pen 6. Elevator 7. Tell or reveal the truth 8. T (train) 9. *Cleopatra* 10. Aslan

Clever Clogs

1 Which dramatist wrote *Pygmalion* and *Arms and the Man*?

2 What sport does Dick Francis write about?

3 Which children's book character lives in Nutwood?

4 Who wrote *Brideshead Revisited*, *Scoop* and *Decline and Fall*?

5 What is the surname of father and son, Kingsley and Martin, who are both writers?

6 What novel, about a large white whale, was written by Herman Melville?

7 What book of facts and statistics, published annually, is known as the bible of the cricket buff?

8 In which book is General Woundwort defeated by Hazel, Bigwig and Fiver?

9 Who wrote the books, adapted into television programmes, about Inspector Morse?

10 Which city does Inspector Morse work in?

TIM, CATCH IT!

Answers

Quiz 36

1 Who wrote spy stories featuring the character George Smiley?

2 In which George Orwell book does Winston Smith and Room 101 appear?

3 Mary Ann Evans wrote *The Mill on the Floss* and *Middlemarch* under what name?

4 Which Irish writer wrote *Ulysses*, *Dubliners* and *A Portrait of the Artist as a Young Man*?

5 Who wrote *Tale of Two Cities*, *Martin Chuzzlewit* and *The Old Curiosity Shop*?

6 Who wrote *Peter Pan*?

7 Which humorous author wrote *Wilt*, *Blott on the Landscape* and *Porterhouse Blue*?

8 Who, according to the Bible, was the oldest man who ever lived?

9 Who wrote *To Kill a Mockingbird*?

10 Which romantic poet wrote about butterflies and daffodils?

Answers

8. Methuselah 9. Harper Lee 10. William Wordsworth

1. John Le Carré 2. 1984 3. George Eliot 4. James Joyce 5. Charles Dickens 6. J.M. Barrie 7. Tom Sharpe

1 How many bags of wool did Baa-baa Black Sheep have in the nursery rhyme?

2 Who was the leader of the Wombles?

3 Which child in the old poem is "full of grace"?

4 Which civil war is the setting for Ernest Hemmingway's *For Whom the Bell Tolls*?

5 What word is an elevator and to raise something?

6 In which Shakespeare play would you have found Yorick: *Hamlet*, *Macbeth* or *King Lear*?

7 Which Conservative politician wrote *The Fourth Estate* and *First Amongst Equals*?

8 What was the name of the girl who met the Mad Hatter and the Queen of Hearts?

9 What was the name of the sword in the *Tales of King Arthur*?

10 In which fairy tale did a girl eat the porridge of the three bears?

Answers

1. Three bags 2. Great Uncle Bulgaria 3. Tuesday's child 4. The Spanish Civil War 5. Lift 6. *Hamlet* 7. Jeffrey Archer 8. Alice 9. Excalibur 10. Goldilocks

Geography

Here are 37 quizzes to test your knowledge of geography. They include questions on different countries and on how the Earth is formed.

The quizzes are divided into three levels of difficulty: Easy Peasy, Clever Clogs and Whiz Kids. As you can probably guess Easy Peasy are the easiest, Clever Clogs the next most difficult and Whiz Kids the hardest. However, the easiest questions are always the ones where you know the answers!

Good luck.

Quiz 1

Easy Peasy

1   In which country are the famous pyramids of the pharaohs situated?

2   What is the capital city of Eire (Southern Ireland)?

3   In what American city is the Empire State Building?

4   Which European country is famous for its beaches and its bull fights?

5   How many states are there in the United States?

6   Which country's cities include Yokohama and Kyoto?

7   What is the name of the continent which includes the countries Chile and Peru?

8   Is cartography: the study of oceans, volcano-watching or map-making?

9   What type of geological feature are Australia, Malta and Iceland?

10 Which country's flag features a red maple leaf?

Answers

1. Egypt 2. Dublin 3. New York 4. Spain 5. 50 6. Japan 7. South America 8. Map-making
9. They are all islands 10. Canada

Quiz 2

1 What is the capital city of Australia?

2 Which European country's flag is a white cross on a red background?

3 What is the name of the second highest mountain in the world?

4 At 110 m, what is Glomach the highest example of in Britain?

5 Which London Underground line is coloured bright red on the map?

6 Is Auckland in New Zealand's North or South Island?

7 In which country would you find the city of Cape Town?

8 What is 4,000 m long and is near Hull?

9 Is the answer to question eight the largest of its kind in Great Britain?

10 If you were driving across the Golden Gate bridge, which city would you be in?

Answers

1. Canberra 2. Switzerland 3. K2 4. Waterfall 5. Central Line 6. North 7. South Africa 8. The Humber Bridge 9. Yes. 10. San Francisco

Quiz 3

1   What is the currency of Cyprus?

2   What is a tributary?

3   What river, first discovered by Christopher Columbus, runs through Venezuela?

4   Which country owns Easter Island?

5   Which state in the USA has its capital based at Tallahassee?

6   With which country would you associate eating vine leaves and drinking retsina?

7   What word describes the time when a volcano becomes very active?

8   What tiny state, just 453 square kilometres in size, is bordered by France and Spain?

9   What is the official capital city of Switzerland?

10 At 5,895 m high, what is the name of the highest mountain in Africa?

Answers

1. The Cyprus pound 2. A stream which runs into a larger river 3. Orinoco 4. Chile 5. Florida 6. Greece 7. Eruption 8. Andorra 9. Bern 10. Mount Kilimanjaro

Quiz 4

1 Where would you find stalactites and stalagmites?

2 Does a stalactite grow up or down?

3 How many centimes are there to a French Franc?

4 If a person was Dutch, which country would they come from?

5 What stretch of sea separates England and France?

6 What is Britain's longest river?

7 Do Eskimos live in the Arctic or Antarctic?

8 What type of weather feature are cirrus and nimbus?

9 What London transport system features the Piccadilly and Northern Lines?

10 What is the capital of Italy?

ERM... I THINK I NEED A LONGER RULER.

Answers

1. In caves 2. Down 3. 100 4. Holland 5. The English Channel 6. River Thames 7. Arctic 8. Clouds 9. London Underground 10. Rome

Quiz 5

1 In which continent are Brunei and Laos?

2 Near which British city is the maze of roads known as Spaghetti Junction?

3 Which country's currency is the drachma?

4 Which group of islands contain Sark and Alderney?

5 Which European country does the River Ebro run through?

6 In which English county are the towns of Deal and Ramsgate?

7 What is the capital of Thailand?

8 What African country has the largest population?

9 What sea separates Australia and New Zealand?

10 What stretch of water separates the Isle of Wight from mainland England?

Answers

1. Asia 2. Birmingham 3. Greece 4. The Channel Islands 5. Spain 6. Kent 7. Bangkok 8. Nigeria 9. The Tasman Sea 10. The Solent

87

Quiz 6

1 What term describes a volcano which has not been active for a time?

2 Which city is situated on the River Mersey?

3 What continent includes Tonga, Fiji and New Zealand?

4 What is the capital of Turkey?

5 What is Turkey's most famous city?

6 What is the largest lake in North America?

7 What is the longest river in the world?

8 Is the Australian state of Tasmania an island?

9 Which country is Budapest the capital city of?

10 What is the name of Russia's national airline?

Answers

1. Dormant 2. Liverpool 3. Oceania 4. Ankara 5. Istanbul 6. Lake Superior 7. The Nile 8. Yes 9. Hungary 10. Aeroflot

Easy Peasy

1 Which English county does Southampton lie in?

2 What country lies directly west of Spain?

3 What is the currency of Italy?

4 In which country would you find the Taj Mahal?

5 Which Scottish lake is allegedly home to Nessie?

6 What is the most populated city in Australia?

7 Where would you find the Eiffel Tower?

8 What is the United Kingdom's national airline?

9 What country is Washington DC the capital of?

10 What important aid to navigation was invented by the Chinese 1,000 years ago?

Answers

1. Hampshire 2. Portugal 3. Lire 4. India 5. Loch Ness 6. Sydney 7. Paris, France 8. British Airways 9. The United States 10. The magnetic compass

Quiz 8

Clever Clogs

1 What Scottish city has the Royal Mile, not far from Waverley station?

2 What major airport, Europe's busiest, is west of the centre of London?

3 In which country would you find organized farms called kibbutz?

4 What island has a capital called Valletta?

5 Which Australian state has Brisbane as its capital?

6 What is the smallest country in Europe?

7 What river, at 3,688 km long, is Europe's longest?

8 What is the capital of the Philippines?

9 What is a tsunami?

10 Which continent contains the Amazon river?

Answers

1. Edinburgh 2. Heathrow 3. Israel 4. Malta 5. Queensland 6. Vatican City 7. The Volga 8. Manila 9. A tidal wave 10. South America

Quiz 9

Whiz Kids

1 Which two large towns does the Grand Union Canal link?

2 How long is the Grand Union Canal?

3 What is the smallest sovereign country in Oceania?

4 What two Mediterranean islands are separated by the Straits of Bonifacio?

5 Which English city, apart from London, has Victoria and Piccadilly stations?

6 What is the third largest ocean?

7 What is the capital of Jersey?

8 What covers about one tenth of all land on Earth at any given time?

9 What collection of 68 islands is also a Scottish county?

10 What type of cloud is towering, dark grey at its base and often gives heavy showers?

YIPEE!!

Quiz 10

1 What is the largest continent in the world?

2 If a person was Peruvian, which country would they come from?

3 In which city would you find Marble Arch and Trafalgar Square?

4 What three colours appear on the French flag?

5 Which country's currency is the Deutsch Mark?

6 What is a glacier?

7 In which continent is the world's largest glacier?

8 The largest gorge in the world is in the United States; what is its name?

9 What geographical feature are the Kalahari and the Atacama examples of?

10 Where does the Massif Central lie — in France, Austria or Switzerland?

Answers

1. Asia 2. Peru 3. London 4. Blue, white and red 5. Germany 6. A huge mass of ice that flows down a mountain valley 7. Antarctica 8. The Grand Canyon 9. Deserts 10. France

Quiz 11

1 Is Manchester Airport, north, west or south of the city?

2 What is the largest town in the English county of Somerset?

3 If you got out of the London Underground at Hatton Cross, what line would you have been travelling on?

4 In which city would you find The White House and the Smithsonian Museum?

5 What is the national airline of Spain?

6 In which English county is Stonehenge?

7 Where is the new Millennium Stadium in Wales?

8 What is the capital of China?

9 What was its former name?

10 In which American state is Hollywood?

Answers

1. South 2. Taunton 3. Piccadilly 4. Washington DC 5. Iberia 6. Wiltshire 7. Cardiff 8. Beijing 9. Peking 10. California

Quiz 12

1 How many states are there in Australia?

2 Which country has more cattle than any other?

3 What is the capital of Iceland?

4 If you were in Cuzco visiting the sites of the Incas, in which country would you be?

5 What name is frequently given to Northern Ireland?

6 In which English county is Corfe Castle?

7 What is the smallest sovereign country in the continent of Africa?

8 Where is Linz?

9 What British lake has an area of 396 km?

10 What African country's capital city is called Lusaka?

Answers

1. Eight 2. India 3. Reykjavik 4. Peru 5. Ulster 6. Dorset 7. Seychelles 8. Austria 9. Lough Neath 10. Zambia

Easy Peasy

1 Where is Mount Snowdon?

2 Which two countries does Hadrian's Wall separate?

3 If you were at King's Cross railway station in London, would you be getting on a train that heads north, south or east?

4 What is the capital of Spain?

5 In which ocean are the islands of Hawaii situated?

6 What Scottish city is famous for its summer festival of the arts?

7 Which country's flag is a red circle on a white background?

8 In which country are the native people called Maoris?

9 In which country is Euro-Disney situated?

10 Which American city is called "the windy city"?

Answers

1. Wales 2. England and Scotland 3. North 4. Madrid 5. The Pacific 6. Edinburgh 7. Japan 8. New Zealand 9. France 10. Chicago

Quiz 14

1 If you were a Geordie, from what area of Britain were you likely to come from?

2 In which Australian state is the city of Melbourne situated?

3 If your plane landed at O'Hare airport, which city would you have arrived in?

4 On which motorway would you find Watford Gap services?

5 Which English county is known as the "garden of England"?

6 What is the capital city of Peru?

7 Which two countries does Lake Geneva border?

8 Which is the world's largest city?

9 If you were taking photos in Red Square, which city would you be in?

10 In which country would you find the lace-makers of Bruges and the port of Antwerp?

Answers

1. Newcastle-upon-Tyne 2. Victoria 3. Chicago 4. The M1 5. Kent 6. Lima 7. Switzerland and France 8. Tokyo 9. Moscow 10. Belgium

1 Which northern Scottish city is famous for its connections with the oil industry?

2 What is the unit of currency of Argentina?

3 The area of Britain which includes Ipswich and Norwich is known by what regional name?

4 In which city are the skyscrapers the Chrysler Building and the Woolworth Building?

5 Where does the Grimaldi family rule?

6 What are the Quantocks?

7 Where is the southernmost tip of Great Britain?

8 What are the counties of Cornwall, Devon, Somerset and Dorset sometimes known as?

9 What does the Beaufort scale measure?

10 On the Beaufort scale, what is 12 an example of?

Answers

1. Aberdeen 2. Peso 3. East Anglia 4. New York 5. Monaco 6. A hill range 7. Land's End 8. The West Country 9. Wind speed 10. A hurricane

Quiz 16

1. Ibiza is a popular holiday island in the Mediterranean Sea. Which country owns it?

2. From which country do Aborigines come from?

3. In which ocean would you find Fiji and Papua New Guinea?

4. Where would you find the Louvre museum which houses the original *Mona Lisa* painting?

5. Which city would you be in if you were standing on the harbour bridge looking at the opera house?

6. Which European country's currency is the drachma?

7. In which country would you find the Great Wall?

8. If you went on holiday in Provence or the Dordogne, in which country would you be?

9. What English county includes the towns Penzance, St Ives and Truro?

10. From London which direction does the M4 take drivers?

Answers

1. Spain 2. Australia 3. Pacific 4. Paris, France 5. Sydney, Australia 6. Greece 7. China 8. France 9. Cornwall 10. West

Quiz 17

1　What is the name of the motorway ring road around Manchester?

2　Which country in the British Isles features the highest point?

3　When molten rock is forced upwards, cools and becomes solid, what is it called?

4　What long wooden tube do Aborigines use to make a sort of music?

5　What country's currency is the yen?

6　What is the largest volcano in the world?

7　In which group of islands can it be found?

8　In which country is the Muslim holy city of Mecca?

9　If your plane landed at Orly airport, which city would you have arrived in?

10　Which country's population is estimated at 1.4 billion?

Answers

1. M60 2. Scotland (Ben Nevis) 3. Igneous 4. Didgeridoo 5. Japan 6. Mauna Loa 7. The Hawaiian Islands 8. Saudi Arabia 9. Paris, France 10. China

Quiz 18

1 What large island lies to the east of Mozambique in Africa?

2 What is the largest country in Africa?

3 What was the country of Zimbabwe formerly called?

4 What is the longest river in the Indian subcontinent?

5 What is the capital city of Ecuador?

6 What covers just 6% of the Earth's surface yet contains 75% of all known species of plants and animals?

7 What is the capital of the Ukraine?

8 What does an anemometer measure?

9 In which country is Mount McKinley the highest peak?

10 Which Eastern European country's currency is the zloty?

Answers

9. United States 10. Poland

1. Madagascar 2. Sudan 3. Rhodesia 4. The Indus 5. Quito 6. Rainforest 7. Kiev 8. Wind speed

Quiz 19

1 Which continent has 17,700 km of coastline and includes the features Vinson Massif and Ross Island?

2 Where would you find the Black Forest?

3 What country is sandwiched between France and the Netherlands?

4 What is that country's capital city?

5 Which Scandinavian country's flag is a yellow cross on a blue background?

6 What is the national airline of Germany?

7 What currency do Canadians use?

8 If land is called agricultural, what is it used for?

9 What is measured in centigrade?

10 Which country's flag is known as the star-spangled banner?

Answers

1. Antarctica 2. Germany 3. Belgium 4. Brussels 5. Sweden 6. Lufthansa 7. Canadian dollars and cents 8. Farming 9. Temperature 10. The United States

Quiz 20

1 Which war-torn country has Zagreb as its capital?

2 What claim to fame does the desert area of Arica have?

3 In which country is Arica?

4 What lake is situated in the middle of Hyde Park in London?

5 What types of rock are sandstone and limestone?

6 How thick is the South Pole ice cap: 50 m, 150 m or 1,500 m?

7 Which canal connects the Mediterranean Sea to the Red Sea?

8 Through which country does it run?

9 What is demography the study of?

10 What three colours make up the Italian flag?

Answers

7. The Suez canal 8. Egypt 9. Populations 10. Green, white and red
1. Croatia 2. The driest place on Earth 3. Chile 4. The Serpentine 5. Sedimentary 6. 1,500 m

1 Which country has 19 major languages and includes the cities of Bangalore and Kanpur?

2 What is the capital of Sri Lanka?

3 Which is the smallest US state?

4 Which country was formerly called Siam?

5 On which river does the Canadian city of Quebec stand?

6 In which country would you find the city of Kathmandu?

7 What country's capital city is Phnom Penn?

8 What is a tor?

9 What term means the ocean surface?

10 Which country's capital city is Bogotá?

Answers

1. India 2. Colombo 3. Rhode Island 4. Thailand 5. St Lawrence 6. Nepal 7. Cambodia 8. A mass of rock on top of a hill 9. Sea level 10. Colombia

Quiz 22

1. In which country would you be if you were on the beaches of Benidorm or the Costa del Sol?

2. Off which country's coast is the island of Anglesey?

3. Which is the largest country in North America?

4. What is the capital of Portugal?

5. There are two official languages of Belgium; one is Flemish, what is the other?

6. What continent features the most people?

7. What Scandinavian country's capital city is Helsinki?

8. Which city in Europe has the biggest population: Paris, London or Bonn?

9. In which continent has the lowest-ever temperature on Earth been recorded?

10. Was that temperature —45 degrees, —90 degrees or —180 degrees centigrade?

Answers

10. — 90 degrees

1. Spain 2. Wales 3. Canada 4. Lisbon 5. French 6. Asia 7. Finland 8. London 9. Antarctica

Quiz 23

1 In which country is the rainiest place on Earth?

2 How much rain does this place receive every year; 1,500 mm, 2,000 mm or 11,000 mm?

3 Which American state has two coastlines – one facing the Atlantic Ocean and the other facing the Gulf of Mexico?

4 What does a barometer measure?

5 What map scale would offer you more detail: 1:50,000 or a 1:500?

6 Is London or Sheffield closer to Birmingham?

7 What stretch of water does the city of Edinburgh overlook?

8 What is the smallest of the world's four oceans?

9 What name do we give to a natural hot water fountain?

10 In which English county would you find the national park of Dartmoor?

Answers

1. Bangladesh 2. 11,000 mm 3. Florida 4. Atmospheric pressure 5. 1:500 6. Sheffield 7. Firth of Forth 8. Arctic Ocean 9. Geyser 10. Devon

Quiz 24

1 What colour flag is flown on a beach declared clean and free of avoidable pollution?

2 Which Welsh county contains Newport and Pontypool?

3 535 active versions of these exist on Earth, 80 of them underwater; what are they?

4 Which Asian country has the capital city of Ulan Bator?

5 What is the name of the world's highest lake?

6 Which two countries does it span?

7 In which continent would you be if you were on the island of Kiribati?

8 What is a fjord?

9 Which country's capital city is Kabul?

10 In which country would you find the holiday resort of Eilat?

Answers

1. Blue 2. Gwent 3. Active volcanoes 4. Mongolia 5. Lake Titicaca 6. Peru and Bolivia 7. Oceania 8. A long, narrow, coastal inlet 9. Afghanistan 10. Israel

Quiz 25

1 Which country has the bullet train?

2 What is the name of the world's biggest desert which covers much of North Africa?

3 Discounting Australia, what is the largest island in the world?

4 In which continent do the Masai and Zulu people live?

5 What word describes when rocks get worn away?

6 What French and British towns offer the shortest route between the two countries?

7 In which country would you find Uluru (formerly Ayers Rock)?

8 Where do the Sherpa people live: Siberia, Nepal or Malaysia?

9 Which country's national airline is KLM?

10 In which city would you find Times Square and Manhattan?

Answers

1. Japan 2. Sahara desert 3. Greenland 4. Africa 5. Erosion 6. Calais and Dover 7. Australia 8. Nepal 9. The Netherlands 10. New York

Quiz 26

1. What is the imaginary circle drawn around the world the same distance from both poles?

2. JAL is the national airline of which country?

3. What is the largest state in the United States?

4. What is the name of the highest waterfall in the world?

5. Which islands are found in the South Atlantic and still have their ownership disputed?

6. Which two countries lay claim to owning these islands?

7. Was the largest recorded iceberg bigger or smaller than Belgium?

8. What island has the capital of Douglas?

9. In which sea would you find the above island?

10. In which continent would you find Niagara Falls?

Answers

1. The Equator 2. Japan 3. Alaska 4. Angel Falls 5. The Falklands 6. Argentina and Britain 7. Bigger 8. Isle of Man 9. Irish Sea 10. America

Quiz 27

1 What holds about 230,000 cubic kilometres of water?

2 What is the highest mountain in Oceania?

3 In which country is it situated?

4 What language do the majority of people speak in Guatemala?

5 What is the capital city of Bulgaria?

6 What is Canada's smallest province?

7 What is the second largest desert in the world?

8 Is Zambia in the Northern or Southern Hemisphere?

9 What killed 45,000 people in northern Armenia in 1988?

10 What is the largest lake in Africa?

Answers

1. The world's rivers 2. Mount Wilhelm 3. Papua New Guinea 4. Spanish 5. Sofia 6. Prince Edward Island 7. The Australian desert 8. Southern 9. An earthquake 10. Lake Victoria

Quiz 28

1 In which country would you find the town of Pisa?

2 What is Pisa's most famous building?

3 What English county neighbours Cornwall?

4 What is the capital of Norway?

5 Which country's currency is the peseta?

6 Which country's capital city is called Brasilia?

7 What ocean separates Europe and North America?

8 In what continent would you find the Alps?

9 What are the Alps?

10 What is the name of the very hot fluid which comes out of a volcano?

Answers

1. Italy 2. The Leaning Tower 3. Devon 4. Oslo 5. Spain 6. Brazil 7. The Atlantic 8. Europe 9. A mountain range 10. Lava

Quiz 29

1. Which Asian country's currency is the baht?
2. What sort of boat is found on the canals of Venice?
3. What is notable about the Mariana Trench?
4. In which body of water can it be found?
5. What does the DC in Washington DC stand for?
6. What sea separates Greece from Turkey?
7. What is the name of the wandering people of the Arabian deserts?
8. Which river flows through the cities of Bonn and Cologne?
9. In which Australian state is the town of Hobart?
10. Where is Damascus?

Answers

1. Thailand 2. Gondola 3. It is the deepest part of the ocean yet found 4. Pacific Ocean 5. District of Columbia 6. Aegean 7. Bedouin 8. The Rhine 9. Tasmania 10. Syria

Quiz 30

Whiz Kids

1 On which ocean does the coast of Tanzania lie?

2 What European country's currency is the escudo?

3 In what part of Britain would you be if you were walking alongside Lake Windermere?

4 What mountain chain runs from north to south through much of South America's length?

5 What is a typhoon?

6 On which island is the volcano Mount Etna?

7 What two European countries does the Gulf of Bothnia separate?

8 How many of the world's highest mountains are found in Asia: 7, 17 or 67?

9 What English county are the Mendip Hills situated in?

10 What country's capital city is Islamabad?

Answers

1. Indian Ocean 2. Portugal 3. The Lake District 4. The Andes 5. A violent hurricane 6. Sicily 7. Finland and Sweden 8. 67 9. Somerset 10. Pakistan

Quiz 31

1 What is drizzle?

2 What three colours are found on the flag of Belgium?

3 What do Perth, Darwin and Adelaide all have in common?

4 What is the capital of Mexico?

5 In which country might you eat feta cheese after visiting the Parthenon?

6 What European country's currency is the schilling?

7 What is a low place in between hills called?

8 Which river flows through the city of Paris?

9 Does the island of Corsica belong to France or Italy?

10 In which country might you eat bird's nest soup after visiting Shanghai?

Answers

1. Very light rain 2. Black, yellow and red 3. They are all Australian cities 4. Mexico City 5. Greece 6. Austria 7. A valley 8. The Seine 9. France 10. China

Easy Peasy

Quiz 32

1 In which English county would you find Blackpool?

2 What city is situated on the River Clyde?

3 From what product does Kuwait derive most of its income?

4 What is the capital of Denmark?

5 Which mountains divide France and Spain?

6 Which is the largest country in the Middle East?

7 In which city are there more canals: Venice or Birmingham?

8 Which US state is directly north of California?

9 What is the Matterhorn?

10 In which country is the port of Antwerp?

Answers

1. Lancashire 2. Glasgow 3. Oil 4. Copenhagen 5. The Pyrenees 6. Saudi Arabia 7. Birmingham 8. Oregon 9. A mountain in the Alps 10. Belgium

1 What is measured on the Richter scale?

2 What is the largest of the Australian states?

3 What is the term used to describe the cooling effect of wind on the skin?

4 Which South American country's name means land of silver?

5 What are antipodes?

6 Which German city was divided by a wall for 40 years?

7 Where in England would you find the Golden Mile?

8 What Asian country, with the capital city of Jakarta, has over 170 million inhabitants?

9. In which place in Britain would you find the Bull Ring and New Street railway station?

10 What is the longest river in Asia?

Answers

1. Earthquakes 2. Western Australia 3. Wind chill 4. Argentina 5. Two places on opposite sides of the Earth 6. Berlin 7. Blackpool 8. Indonesia 9. Birmingham 10. Yangtzee (Chang Jiang) river in China

Quiz 34

1 If you were travelling from Los Angeles to visit the original Disneyland, what American state would you be in?

2 Which country produces more coffee than any other?

3 Antrim, Armagh or Londonderry are in which part of the United Kingdom?

4 What is the capital of Wales?

5 Inside which Italian place is the Vatican City situated?

6 What continent is one and a half times bigger than the United States?

7 How many African countries does the Equator pass through: two, thirteen or six?

8 If you were cycling through Amsterdam, which country would you be visiting?

9 Which US state includes the city of Dallas and is known as the "Lone Star State"?

10 In what country is the region of Normandy?

Answers

1. California 2. Brazil 3. Northern Ireland 4. Cardiff 5. Rome 6. Antarctica 7. Six 8. The Netherlands 9. Texas 10. France

Clever Clogs

1 What feature of seas does the Moon have an affect on?

2 What is the most common language spoken on Earth?

3 Which ocean is the island of Tahiti in?

4 What is the capital of Malaysia?

5 Which country's national airline is Varig?

6 What is the world's longest country?

7 In which country would you be if you were travelling from Marrakesh to Fès?

8 In what country is the world's coldest city?

9 What does a seismograph measure?

10 In which country, beginning with the letter M, is Timbuktu situated?

Answers

1. The tides 2. Mandarin 3. Pacific Ocean 4. Kuala Lumpur 5. Brazil 6. Chile 7. Morocco 8. Mongolia 9. Earthquakes 10. Mali

Quiz 36

1 Which region includes parts of Norway, Russia, Sweden and Finland?

2 What is the measurement and mapping of the Earth called?

3 What country has four times as many pigs as any other nation?

4 In which country is the world's second-highest mountain situated?

5 Where is the Ross Ice Shelf?

6 Which African country is the most popular safari destination in the world?

7 What gruesome name is given to the United States hottest place?

8 In which sea would you find St Lucia and Trinidad and Tobago?

9 What is the capital of Zimbabwe?

10 If you were admiring the Church of St Basil, in which major city would you be?

AND HERE WE SEE ONE OF THE MOST FEROCIOUS PREDATORS OF THE AFRICAN PLAIN.

Answers

1. Lapland 2. Surveying 3. China 4. Pakistan 5. Antartica 6. Kenya 7. Death Valley 8. The Caribbean 9. Harare 10. Moscow

Quiz 37

1 What is called London's third airport?

2 In what part of London is the Millennium Dome situated?

3 What London Underground line's most northern station is Walthamstow?

4 What is a monsoon?

5 What country is bordered by China and the former USSR?

6 What North African country has the capital city of Tripoli?

7 Which country is the leading coal producer in the world?

8 From what country did Christopher Columbus set sail?

9 In which ocean is the world's deepest underwater trench?

10 In which country is Shensi Province?

Answers

1. Stansted 2. Greenwich 3. Victoria line 4. A wind which brings heavy rains 5. Mongolia 6. Libya 7. USA 8. Spain 9. Pacific Ocean 10. China

Sports & Entertainment

Here are 37 quizzes to see what you know about sports and entertainment. They include questions on television programmes, pop music, and a whole variety of sports and sports personalities.

The quizzes are divided into three levels of difficulty: Easy Peasy, Clever Clogs and Whiz Kids. As you can probably guess Easy Peasy are the easiest, Clever Clogs the next most difficult and Whiz Kids the hardest. However, the easiest questions are always the ones where you know the answers!

Good luck.

Quiz 1

1. What is the real name of the singer formerly known as Ginger Spice?

2. How many points is the bulls-eye worth in darts?

3. What is the name of the spaceman in *Toy Story 2*?

4. In what TV show would you find characters called Marg and Homer?

5. What is a hundred runs called in cricket?

6. What is the name of the teenage witch who lives with her aunts and a talking cat?

7. Which football team plays at White Hart Lane?

8. Which films featured terrifying creatures called Raptors?

9. Which football team didn't enter the 1999/2000 FA Cup?

10. Where would you find a hoop, a backboard and a three point line?

Answers

1. Geri Halliwell 2. 50 3. Buzz Lightyear 4. *The Simpsons* 5. A century 6. Sabrina 7. Tottenham Hotspur 8. *Jurassic Park* 9. Manchester United 10. A basketball court

Quiz 2

1 Which football club has Elton John as its chairman?

2 What town do the Flintstones come from?

3 Which famous boxer was voted sportsperson of the millennium?

4 Which famous singer is co-manager of the boyband, Westlife?

5 Which Formula One team is managed by Ron Dennis?

6 Which famous Australian fast bowler once tried to use an aluminium bat?

7 What is the most expensive property on a Monopoly board?

8 How many points are given for a rugby union drop goal?

9 Which football team have the nickname "the Owls"?

10 Which comic actor played Fletcher in *Porridge* and Arkwright in *Open All Hours*?

Answers

1. Watford 2. Bedrock 3. Muhammad Ali 4. Ronan Keating 5. McClaren 6. Dennis Lillee 7. Mayfair 8. Three 9. Sheffield Wednesday 10. Ronnie Barker

Quiz 3

1 Westlife's single, *I Had A Dream*, was performed in the 1970s by which band?

2 What space is diagonally opposite Go on a Monopoly board?

3 How many grand slam tournaments are there in tennis?

4 Which successful Scottish football club did Sir Alex Ferguson manage before Manchester United?

5 Kobe Bryant, Magic Johnson and Wilt Chamberlain all played which sport?

6 How many members are there in the boyband Point Break?

7 If you had a mashie and a niblick in your bag, what sport would you be playing?

8 What TV show features the characters Xander, Willow and Angel?

9 Which national cricket team featured the talented Crowe brothers?

10 Which rugby league club plays at the JJB Stadium?

Answers

1. Abba 2. Free parking 3. Four 4. Aberdeen 5. Basketball 6. Three 7. Golf 8. *Buffy the Vampire Slayer* 9. New Zealand 10. Wigan

Quiz 4

1 How many pockets are there on a snooker table?

2 Which football team play at Elland Road?

3 Which show features two sets of flat-sharing pals?

4 Which actor/rapper recorded an album called *Willennium*?

5 What sport did *Gladiators* presenter John Fashanu once play professionally?

6 What nationality is the band Catatonia?

7 Which nation's rugby team are known as the All Blacks?

8 What was the title of Westlife's debut album?

9 Which country does batsman Sachin Tendulkar play for?

10 What TV show features Laurence, Carol and Handy Andy?

Answers

1. Six. 2. Leeds United 3. *Friends* 4. Will Smith 5. Football 6. Welsh 7. New Zealand 8. *Westlife* 9. India 10. *Changing Rooms*

Quiz 5

1 Which British rower is going for a world record number of Olympic gold medals?

2 Which TV show features a radio psychologist who lives with his father, his father's dog and a home help?

3 Which former England cricket captain is now a team captain on a comedy quiz show?

4 What county did he play cricket for?

5 Who directed the films *Jackie Brown* and *Reservoir Dogs*?

6 How many players in an Australian Rules team: 12, 15 or 18?

7 In which band did Bill Wyman play for over twenty years?

8 Richard Dunwoody is a leading participant in which sport?

9 What leisure pursuit comes in coarse, fly and sea forms?

10 Which fez-wearing comedian had the catchphrase "Just like that"?

Answers

1. Steve Redgrave 2. *Frasier* 3. David Gower 4. Leicestershire 5. Quentin Tarantino 6. 18 7. The Rolling Stones 8. Horse-racing 9. Fishing 10. Tommy Cooper

Quiz 6

1   Who finished second in the 1999 Formula One Championship?

2   Whose smash 1999 album was entitled *Come On Over*?

3   Which British tennis player was beaten by Chris Woodruff in the 2000 Australian Open?

4   In golf, what is a hole completed in one under par called?

5   Which American female singer starred in the film *The Bodyguard*?

6   Who hosts the show *Masterchef*?

7   What is the name of the Sunday newspaper that only covers sport?

8   Who won the 1999 Football League Cup?

9   Which film actress is married to Tom Cruise?

10 Who did Manchester United beat in the final of the 1999 European Champions League?

Answers

1. Eddie Irvine 2. Shania Twain 3. Tim Henman 4. A birdie 5. Whitney Houston 6. Loyd Grossman 7. *Sport First* 8. Tottenham Hotspur 9. Nicole Kidman 10. Bayern Munich

Quiz 7

Easy Peasy

1. How many dalmations were there in the famous Disney film?

2. What nationality is fast bowler Allan Donald?

3. What was Winnie the Pooh's favourite food?

4. What sport does *Question of Sport* captain, John Parrott play?

5. Which country does footballer Ronaldo play for?

6. Where is Britain's one tennis grand slam tournament played?

7. Pixie and Trixie starred in a cartoon with a cat; what was its name?

8. What is the name of the only Welsh county cricket team?

9. Which TV show features the characters Dot Cotton and Phil Mitchell?

10. What are Monza and Brands Hatch?

Answers

Quiz 8

1   How many points is a blue ball worth in snooker?

2   If you saw three slips and a gully, amongst others, what sport would you be watching?

3   Which cartoon rabbit is always seen chewing carrots?

4   Which football team play at Villa Park?

5   Which action hero starred in the *Die Hard* series of films?

6   With which sport are promoters, Frank Warren and Don King associated?

7   What is the name of Batman's road vehicle?

8   Which film star first shot to fame playing a disco star in *Saturday Night Fever*?

9   Who is the manager of Leeds United football club?

10 In what sport do you get three strikes before you are out?

Answers

1. Five 2. Cricket 3. Bugs Bunny 4. Aston Villa 5. Bruce Willis 6. Boxing 7. The Batmobile 8. John Travolta 9. David O'Leary 10. Baseball

Whiz Kids

1 Who was the first player to hit six sixes off one over in cricket?

2 Which sport features teams of ten with up to 13 substitutes, all wearing protective helmets?

3 Can you name the teenage son in the TV show *The Royle Family*?

4 How many Test cricket nations are there?

5 What was the name of the postman in the series *Cheers*?

6 Which *Toy Story* character does the same actor provide the voice for?

7 Which *Friends* character is played by actor David Schwimmer?

8 What three events occur on the second day of a women's heptathlon?

9 In what year did Jesse Owens win four Olympic gold medals in running events and the long jump?

10 Who did Lisa Tarbuck replace on *The Big Breakfast*?

Answers

1. Sir Garfield Sobers 2. Lacrosse 3. Anthony 4. Nine 5. Cliff (Clavin) 6. Mr Potato Head 7. Ross 8. Long jump, javelin and 800m 9. 1936 10. Kelly Brook

Quiz 10

1 Is Phil Tufnell a fast or spin bowler?

2 Which football team do Kanu and Ray Parlour play for?

3 What type of creature is the computer game character Sonic?

4 Which city did the Beatles come from?

5 Who was the shy dwarf in *Snow White*?

6 How many teams are relegated from the Premiership every year?

7 Which TV show features Del Boy and Rodney Trotter?

8 Which elephant could fly?

9 In what sport would you use parallel bars?

10 When were the Olympic Games held in Barcelona?

Answers

1. Spin bowler 2. Arsenal 3. A hedgehog 4. Liverpool 5. Bashful 6. Three 7. Only Fools and Horses 8. Dumbo 9. Gymnastics 10. 1992

Quiz 11

1 What athletics discipline was Sally Gunnell famous for?

2 Who is the female host of *Ready, Steady, Cook*?

3 Where were the 1996 Olympics held?

4 What sport do the brothers Scott and Craig Quinnell play?

5 What is the name of the plastic peg used to raise the ball in golf?

6 Who plays Scully in the show *The X Files*?

7 Which football team play at Maine Road?

8 How many times a normal score are the red squares worth on a Scrabble board?

9 Which TV soap features a mother and son called Kathy and Ian?

10 How many pieces are there on a draught or checkers board at the start?

Answers

1. 400m hurdles 2. Fern Britten 3. Atlanta, USA 4. Rugby union 5. A tee 6. Gillian Anderson 7. Manchester City 8. Three times the word 9. *EastEnders* (the Beales) 10. 24.

Quiz 12

1 Who was named 1999 world footballer of the year by FIFA?

2 In which sport might a Fosbury Flop be performed?

3 Which rugby team play at The Stoop?

4 Which *Friends* star appeared in the movie *Lost in Space*?

5 Which French football star appears in shampoo commercials and *Stars in Their Eyes*?

6 How many players are there in a rugby league team?

7 What is Britain's largest record company?

8 Which Scottish footballer sits alongside Gary Lineker on *Match of the Day*?

9 Where would you find The Chair and Beecher's Brook?

10 How many series of *Blackadder* were there?

Answers

1. Rivaldo 2. The High Jump 3. Harlequins 4. Matt Le Blanc (Joey in *Friends*) 5. David Ginola 6. 13 7. EMI 8. Alan Hansen 9. Aintree racecourse 10. Four

Quiz 13

1   What was so amazing about the pig called Babe?

2   What weight did Frank Bruno used to box at?

3   What doctor had a phone box for a time machine?

4   What is the name of Sunderland football club's stadium?

5   Which country won the 1998 football World Cup?

6   Who played Blackadder in the TV series?

7   What type of hat did Laurel and Hardy both wear?

8   Which county does batsman/wicketkeeper Alec Stewart play for?

9   How many dwarves featured in the story of *Snow White*?

10   How many points is the pink ball worth in snooker?

Answers

1. It could talk 2. Heavyweight 3. Dr Who 4. The Stadium of Light 5. France 6. Rowan Atkinson 7. A bowler hat 8. Surrey 9. Seven 10. Six

Quiz 14

Clever Clogs

1. Who is Batman's sidekick?
2. Who is the world number one in golf?
3. What sport does Ian Botham's son, Liam, play?
4. What was the name of Fred Flintstone's next door neighbour and buddy?
5. How many holes on a standard golf course?
6. What type of creature was the star of *Jaws*?
7. In what decade is the comedy drama *The Grimleys* set?
8. What country does Ryan Giggs play for?
9. What sport are Duncan Goodhew and Mark Foster associated with?
10. Which Australian entertainer hosts a show about animal hospitals?

Answers

1. Robin 2. Tiger Woods 3. Rugby union 4. Barney Rubble 5. 18 6. A shark 7. The 1970s 8. Wales 9. Swimming 10. Rolf Harris

Quiz 15

1 Who played Batman in the 1989 film of the same name?

2 Which 1980s American soap opera featured Sue Ellen and Bobby?

3 Who was the manager of Chelsea football club before Gianluca Vialli?

4 Which radio station features disc jockey Terry Wogan?

5 Which glam rock singer is now a star in the show *The Grimleys*?

6 Where was the first race of the 2000 Formula One season held?

7 Which TV personality has a brother called Paul, also a TV presenter?

8 In what sport could you perform a triple toe loop?

9 Which controversial comedy/drama is set in a fictional town called Royston Vasey?

10 Who played Fred Flintstone in the live action film of the cartoon?

Answers

1. Michael Keaton 2. *Dallas* 3. Ruud Gullit 4. Radio Two 5. Noddy Holder of Slade 6. Melbourne, Australia 7. Jonathon Ross 8. Ice skating 9. *The League of Gentlemen* 10. John Goodman

Quiz 16

1 What was the name of the big bear in *The Jungle Book*?

2 Which sports stadium is to have its twin towers torn down soon for redevelopment?

3 Which county cricket side do Darren Gough and Chris Silverwood play for?

4 What Australian TV programme occurs largely on Ramsey Street?

5 What was the name of Mickey Mouse's dog?

6 Which chess piece can only move diagonally?

7 Who is Yogi Bear's pint-sized pal?

8 Which band features Bono and The Edge?

9 What is the name of the sand-filled depressions around a golf course?

10 Which Hollywood film actress starred in *Notting Hill*?

Answers

9. Bunkers 10. Julia Roberts

1. Baloo 2. Wembley stadium 3. Yorkshire 4. *Neighbours* 5. Pluto 6. The bishop 7. Boo-Boo 8. U2

Quiz 17

1 What are the first names of the tennis-playing Williams sisters?

2 What city did Batman do his best to protect?

3 Which county cricket side plays at Headingley?

4 What was Superman's ordinary name?

5 In what sport can competitors use the Fosbury Flop or the Western Roll?

6 Which band was Gary Barlow in before he went solo?

7 Which American tennis player was famous for his on-court tantrums?

8 Ventriloquist Bob Carolgees has a dog puppet with a revolting habit; what is its name?

9 What is the world's most-watched cycling competition?

10 Who wrote the music for the musicals *Cats* and *Starlight Express*?

Answers

1. Serena and Venus 2. Gotham City 3. Yorkshire 4. Clark Kent 5. High jump 6. Take That 7. John McEnroe 8. Spit 9. Tour de France 10. Andrew Lloyd-Webber

Quiz 18

Whiz Kids

1. Which children's programme once featured John Noakes, Lesley Judd and Peter Duncan?

2. How many points would you score if you made a maximum break in snooker?

3. Who played the Penguin in the film *Batman Returns*?

4. What TV show made Pamela Lee Anderson a star?

5. What square is diagonally opposite the Go to Jail square on a Monopoly board?

6. In what sport would you find a jack and a mat?

7. On what radio station would you find the *Today* programme and *The Archers*?

8. What bird is the symbol of the French rugby team?

9. Which ex-Arsenal and England striker has his own chat show?

10. Of which band is Damon Albarn the lead singer?

Answers

1. Blue Peter 2. 147 3. Danny DeVito 4. Baywatch 5. Jail 6. Bowls 7. Radio Four 8. A cockerel 9. Ian Wright 10. Blur

Quiz 19

Easy Peasy

1 What is the name of the bear in *The Muppets*?

2 Which country does Brian Lara play cricket for?

3 What cat is always looking to catch and eat Tweetie-Pie?

4 Who plays football at The Dell?

5 In what sort of building is the TV show *ER* set?

6 If you are out for no runs in cricket, what is it called?

7 Which children's programme features Grover and Big Bird?

8 What show about aliens and conspiracies features agent Mulder?

9 What is the name given to the first shot in a tennis rally?

10 What sport features downhill and slalom competitions?

Answers

1. Fozzie 2. West Indies 3. Sylvester 4. Southampton 5. A hospital 6. A duck 7. Sesame Street 8. The X Files 9. Serve 10. Skiing

139

Quiz 20

1 What sport features the teams Utah Jazz and Chicago Bulls?

2 Which boyband were named after the postcode of London where they came from?

3 What is the name give to someone who runs onto a sports pitch with no clothes on?

4 Which female singer had hits with *Honey to a Bee* and *Girlfriend*?

5 In football, what is the small rectangle inside the penalty area called?

6 Which TV soap is set in and around the town of Chester?

7 Who is lead singer of the band REM?

8 Which county cricket side has wicketkeeper Jack Russell played for all his career?

9 What nationality is rugby player Jonah Lomu?

10 Who hosts the TV series *Robot Wars*?

Answers

1. Basketball in America 2. E17 3. A streaker 4. Billie 5. Six yard box 6. *Hollyoaks* 7. Michael Stipe 8. Gloucestershire 9. New Zealand 10. Craig Charles and Philippa Forrester

Whiz Kids

1 What was the name of the newspaper Superman worked on?

2 Who plays at the Noucamp stadium?

3 Who directed the first *Batman* film?

4 In what sport does a cox control his or her team?

5 What sport includes the teams Buffalo Bills, Miami Dolphins and the Washington Redskins?

6 Name Kermit the frog's cousin who sang *Halfway up the Stairs?*

7 Who was the captain of the French 1998 World Cup football side?

8 What Hollywood film awards are held before the Oscars?

9 In which city was the first World Club Football Championship held?

10 Which new romantic band did *EastEnders* star Martin Kemp used to play in?

Answers

1. *The Daily Planet* 2. Barcelona football club 3. Tim Burton 4. Rowing 5. American Football 6. Robin 7. Zinedine Zidane 8. The Golden Globes 9. Rio, Brazil 10. Spandau Ballet

Quiz 22

1 Which male German tennis player retired from the game in 1999?

2 What computer game requires the player to arrange different-shaped falling blocks?

3 What sport features a quarterback and touchdowns?

4 What swimming stroke is named after an insect?

5 Which band features brothers Noel and Liam?

6 How many yellow cards equal a red card in football?

7 Which country joined rugby's Five Nations in 2000 to make it Six Nations?

8 With what sport is the venue Twickenham associated?

9 Which duck often accompanies Bugs Bunny in cartoons?

10 What throwing event involves spinning a ball on a metal chain?

Answers

1. Boris Becker 2. *Tetris* 3. American Football 4. Butterfly 5. Oasis 6. Two 7. Italy 8. Rugby Union 9. Daffy 10. The hammer

Quiz 23

1 How many golf shots would you have taken if you had got an eagle on a par 5 hole?

2 The Super Furry Animals and The Stereophonics hail from which country?

3 What TV channel broadcasts Home and Away, Rosie and Jim and Wheel of Fortune?

4 How many wickets must you take in cricket to bowl a side out?

5 What sort of musical instrument are Farfisa and Hammond examples of ?

6 What position in rugby union usually carries the number 15 on the players shirt?

7 Neil Buchanan hosts which popular TV crafts show for kids?

8 Who became the third most expensive football transfer in Britain when he moved from Leicester to Liverpool?

9 Sam Smith is the number one Briton at which sport?

10 Who did Leeds United beat to progress to the quarter finals of the 200 UEFA cup?

Answers

1.Three 2. Wales 3. ITV 4. Ten 5. Electric organ 6. Full Back 7. Art 8. Emile Heskey 9. Womens Tennis 10. Roma

Quiz 24

1 Which TV show features characters called Ned Flanders and Mr Burns?

2 Who is the female narrator on the *Tele Tubbies* show?

3 Which South African cricketer is nicknamed "Zulu"?

4 What is the name of the BBC radio show based in the fictional town of Ambridge?

5 What did Manchester United replace six times between 1998 and 2000?

6 Which radio station featured live commentary of England's tour of South Africa in 1999/2000?

7 What is the name of the dog in the TV show *Frasier*?

8 Who was cricketer "Merv the Swerve"?

9 What is the name of the character voiced by soul singer Isaac Hayes in *South Park*?

10 Which band had a hit 1999 album with *The Man Who*?

Answers

1. *The Simpsons* 2. Toyah Wilcox 3. Lance Klusener 4. *The Archers* 5. Their pitch 6. Talksport Radio 7. Eddie 8. Merv Hughes, Australian fast bowler 9. Chef 10. Travis

Quiz 25

Easy Peasy

1 In which position did Australian rugby star David Campese mainly play?

2 Which Beatle provided the narration for *Thomas the Tank Engine*?

3 With what sport was Brazilian Ayrton Senna connected?

4 Which actress plays teenage boy Perry alongside Harry Enfield?

5 Where were the 1980 Summer Olympics held?

6 Which singer hosted the one-off TV show *Victoria's Secrets*?

7 What villain did Jack Nicholson play in *Batman*?

8 In athletics, what is 4.9 m long and made of glass fibre?

9 How many points does a team get for an unconverted try in rugby union?

10 Who won an Oscar for his role in the film *Philadelphia*?

Answers

Wing 2. Ringo Starr 3. Formula One 4. Kathy Burke 5. Moscow, Russia 6. Victoria Beckham (Posh Spice) 7. The Joker 8. A pole vault pole 9. Five 10. Tom Hanks

145

Quiz 26

Clever Clogs

1 Who was the England manager at the 1998 World Cup Finals?

2 Which English player was sent off in the quarter finals of that competition?

3 Which team were England playing at the time?

4 How many people are in the band Steps?

5 Which cartoon character is always chasing Yogi Bear?

6 Which long-running duo's first hit was *West End Girls*?

7 Which country do footballers Emmanuel Petit and Patrick Vierra play for?

8 How many overs do each side get in international one-day cricket matches?

9 Which singer played Tiffany in *EastEnders*?

10 They used to be called football linesmen; what are these officials now called?

Answers

1. Glenn Hoddle 2. David Beckham 3. Argentina 4. Five 5. Ranger Smith 6. Pet Shop Boys 7. France 8. 50 9. Martine McCutcheon 10. Referee's assistants

Quiz 27

1 Which female singer used to be in a duo with her husband Sonny Bono?

2 How many stations are there on a Monopoly board?

3 What chess piece is sometimes called a rook?

4 Who has a brother called Niles and a producer of his radio show called Ros?

5 What is the tennis score, technically known as 40-40, called?

6 Who is the star of the computer game *Tomb Raider*?

7 What is the symbol on all Ferrari motor racing cars?

8 Which American comedy about a law firm is named after the character played by Calista Flockart?

9 Which former England World Cup star managed the Republic of Ireland for many years?

10 Which children's programme about animals is hosted by Nick Baker and Michaela Strachan?

Answers

9. Jackie Charlton 10. *The Really Wild Show*

1. Cher 2. Four 3. Castle 4. Frasier Crane 5. Deuce 6. Lara Croft 7. A prancing horse 8. Ally McBeal

Quiz 28

Easy Peasy

1 Which singing group features Faye, H, Lee, Claire and Lisa?

2 How long is a regular football match?

3 Which character has appeared in *The World is Not Enough* and *Thunderball*?

4 What country does football star Dennis Bergkamp come from?

5 Which band recorded *Yellow Submarine*, *Help* and *A Hard Day's Night*?

6 In snooker, how many points is the green ball worth?

7 Which American comedy show features Chandler, Monica and Joey?

8 Are boyband Another Level British, Canadian or American?

9 What type of instrument is a Fender Stratocaster?

10 Name one of the two packs of cards in the middle of a Monopoly board?

Answers

1. Steps 2. 90 minutes 3. James Bond 4. Holland 5. The Beatles 6. Three 7. *Friends* 8. British 9. An electric guitar 10. Chance and Community Chest

148

Clever Clogs

1 Which Scottish comedian starred alongside Judi Dench in *Mrs Brown*?

2 How many shots under par is an eagle in golf?

3 Which NBA basketball team did Michael Jordan play for?

4 Which close male friend of Liz Hurley played the male lead in *Notting Hill*?

5 Where does the Scotland rugby union team play their home games?

6 Who played Judge Dredd in the film of the same name?

7 Which Scottish football team plays at Ibrox?

8 Which American actor starred in *Hook, Dead Poets Society* and *The Fisher King*?

9 What was the name of the cartoon character known as the friendly ghost?

10 Which band features Thom Yorke as lead singer?

Answers

1. Billy Connolly 2. Two 3. Chicago Bulls 4. Hugh Grant. 5. Murrayfield 6. Sylvester Stallone 7. Celtic 8. Robin Williams 9. Casper 10. Radiohead

Quiz 30

1 Which country were the first to field a father and son in a football world cup game?

2 Which actress plays the lead in the comedy *Gimme, Gimme, Gimme?*

3 Who were England's last opponents in the 1999 cricket world cup?

4 What is the catchphrase of the male character in *One Foot in the Grave?*

5 Who is the actor who plays him?

6 In which country did Gary Lineker finish his football-playing days?

7 Which Geordie boyband had a hit with the single *Stand Tough?*

8 Which ex-captain of Scotland plays football for Coventry?

9 Which All Saints' single featured in the film *The Beach?*

10 Who was caretaker manager of the England team between Glenn Hoddle and Kevin Keegan?

Answers

1. Iceland 2. Kathy Burke 3. India 4. "I don't believe it!" 5. Richard Wilson 6. Japan 7. Point Break 8. Gary McAllister 9. Pure Shores 10. Howard Wilkinson

Quiz 31

1   What is the maximum number of points allowed in the card game pontoon?

2   Which films feature a cowboy called Woody and Mr Potato Head?

3   Five brothers re-formed their 70's group in 2000 around their most successful member Michael. What is that group's name?

4   Which chess piece can only move one space at a time?

5   Which singing star recorded a controversial version of the Lord's Prayer for Christmas 1999?

6   Which band had hits with *Champagne Supernova* and *Wonderwall*?

7   How many points is a red ball worth in snooker?

8   What country does golfer Sergio Garcia come from?

9   Who won the 1999 Cricket World Cup?

10 Which film series featured M and Miss Moneypenny?

Answers

1. 21 2. *Toy Story* and *Toy Story 2* 3. The Jackson Five 4. King 5. Cliff Richard 6. Oasis 7. One 8. Spain 9. Australia 10. The Bond films

151

Quiz 32

1 Which British Grand Prix driver, the son of a famous racing father, retired in 1999?

2 Which comedian is famous for his impressions of Des Lynam, Dale Winton and Tony Blair?

3 What is the first name of Michael Schumacher's motor-racing younger brother?

4 Who hosts the show *Question of Sport*?

5 What sport did she used to play?

6 How many picture cards in a regular pack of cards?

7 Which other European country is competing to host the 2006 football World Cup Finals?

8 Name the band which features singer Jay Kay?

9 Which country do cricketers Grant Flower and Heath Streak play for?

10 In which long-running comedy show did the character of Frasier first appear?

Answers

1. Damon Hill 2. Rory Bremner 3. Ralf 4. Sue Barker 5. Tennis 6. 12 7. Germany 8. Jamiroqui 9. Zimbabwe 10. Cheers

1   In what town was the TV comedy *Cheers* set?

2   Which new American Football team fought the 2000 Superbowl against the Rams?

3   Who directed the films *Annie Hall*, *Mighty Aphrodite* and *Hannah and her Sisters*?

4   In which city do the Royle Family live?

5   What was Muhammad Ali's original name?

6   Which punk rock band were managed by Malcolm McClaren and had a hit with *Pretty Vacant*?

7   Who is the world champion at chess?

8   What do Monaco, Brands Hatch and Monza have in common?

9   Which modern artist has become famous for cutting sheep and cows in half?

10   In pontoon or blackjack, how many points is a King worth?

Answers

7. Gary Kasparov 8. They are all Grand Prix race tracks 9. Damien Hirst 10. Ten
1. Boston 2. Tennessee Titans 3. Woody Allen 4. Manchester 5. Cassius Clay 6. Sex Pistols

Quiz 34

1 What is the most common piece on a chess board?

2 Name one of the two countries which will co-host the 2002 Football World Cup?

3 Who was in love with Kermit the Frog in *The Muppets*?

4 What game is played on horseback by Prince Charles, amongst others?

5 What football position is associated with Neville Southall, Peter Shilton and Nigel Martyn?

6 Which tennis player challenges Tim Henman for the number one British spot?

7 What seven-a-side sport features Goal Shooters, Goal Defence and Wing Attack positions?

8 In which city is the TV soap *Brookside* set?

9 What national cricket side do Wasim Akram and Saqulain Mushtaq play for?

10 In which sport do players use rackets to hit a shuttle?

Answers

1. Pawns 2. Japan and Korea 3. Miss Piggy 4. Polo 5. Goalkeeper 6. Greg Rusedski 7. Netball 8. Liverpool 9. Pakistan 10. Badminton

Quiz 35

1 Which Australian spin bowler overtook Dennis Lillee's wicket-taking record in 1999?

2 What type of instrument are crash, ride and high-hat examples of?

3 Which English football team plays at The Valley?

4 Which famous composer wrote *Twinkle Twinkle Little Star* at the age of four?

5 What is a table tennis ball made of?

6 What type of event would you be watching if you saw an arabesque and a glissade being performed?

7 How many goals did Pelé score in his career: 800, 1,200 or 2,000?

8 What sport features a line backer and a wide receiver?

9 What is the surname of the computer game character Crash?

10 Hibs and Hearts are two Scottish football teams; in which city are they based?

Answers

1. Shane Warne 2. Cymbals 3. Charlton Athletic 4. Mozart 5. Celluloid 6. Ballet 7. 1,200 8. American Football 9. Bandicoot 10. Edinburgh

Quiz 36

1 Which director made many suspense films including *Vertigo* and *The Birds*?

2 Which Swedish golfer partnered Sergio Garcia in the 1999 Ryder Cup?

3 Who took over from Zoe Ball on Radio One's breakfast show?

4 Which two brothers were in England's 1966 football World Cup-winning team?

5 Which band once featured Phil Collins and Peter Gabriel as lead singers?

6 Which spoof superhero film featured comedian Eddie Izzard as Disco Tony?

7 Which football team did Trevor Sinclair play for before his transfer to West Ham?

8 Which actor starred in *The Full Monty*, *Carla's Song* and *Trainspotting*?

9 If you potted all the colour balls in snooker, excluding the reds, how many points would you score?

10 Name the two actors who play the *Men Behaving Badly*.

Answers

1. Alfred Hitchcock 2. Jesper Parnevik 3. Sara Cox 4. Bobby and Jackie Charlton 5. Genesis 6. *Mystery Men* 7. Queens Park Rangers 8. Robert Carlyle 9. 27 10. Neil Morrissey and Martin Clunes

Quiz 37

1 Which Formula One team had the drivers Eddie Irvine and Johnny Herbert in the 2000 season?

2 Which team lost the 1999 cricket world cup final?

3 Who had hits with *Baby One More Time* and *Sometimes*?

4 What sort of knights appear in the *Star Wars* films?

5 Who won the 1999 Worthington Cup?

6 With which sport do you associate commentator Murray Walker?

7 What is the name of the eldest kid in *Rugrats*?

8 What is the name of the cat in *Sabrina the Teenage Witch*?

9 What sport uses a foil or an épée?

10 Which boyband released the album *Invincible*?

Answers

1. Jaguar 2. Pakistan 3. Britney Spears 4. Jedi 5. Tottenham Hotspur 6. Motor racing 7. Angelica 8. Salem 9. Fencing 10. Five

Natural World

Here are 37 quizzes to see what you know about the natural world. They include questions on how our bodies work, animals, plants, different natural habitats, the environment and so on.

The quizzes are divided into three levels of difficulty: Easy Peasy, Clever Clogs and Whiz Kids. As you can probably guess Easy Peasy are the easiest, Clever Clogs the next most difficult and Whiz Kids the hardest. However, the easiest questions are always the ones where you know the answers!

Good luck.

Quiz 1

1 What type of fruit come in the varieties: Cox's Orange Pippin and Granny Smith's?

2 Are whales fish or mammals?

3 How long does an unborn human baby spend inside its mother?

4 What part of your body features a pupil and a cornea?

5 What mammal makes large dams out of wood?

6 Is a prickly pear: a type of tree, cactus or wallflower?

7 What are the names of the two types of elephant?

8 What type of bird would you find in a gaggle?

9 What is the name given to a female pig?

10 Which land animal is the fastest runner?

Answers

1. Apples 2. Mammals 3. Nine months 4. The eye 5. The beaver 6. A cactus 7. Indian and African 8. Geese 9. Sow 10. The cheetah

Quiz 2

1 Which big cat lives the longest: the lion, the panther or the tiger?

2 Can a dog see colours?

3 What is the eye problem myopia better known as?

4 How many species of acacia tree are there: 15, 60 or 1,200?

5 Which common bird comes in house and tree varieties?

6 Gorillas are found in how many continents?

7 The goliath beetle holds which insect record?

8 What adult creature's body contains 206 bones?

9 What is the largest living creature in the world?

10 What part of a fish is made from spines covered in skin?

Answers

9. The blue whale 10. Fins

1. The lion 2. No 3. Short-sightedness 4. 1,200 5. Sparrow 6. One 7. The heaviest insect 8. Humans

1 Hydroponics is the science of growing plants without what usual component?

2 If a creature is extinct, what does it mean?

3 What is the claw of a bird of prey called?

4 What name is given to a male horse under the age of four?

5 What is the name given to a male giraffe?

6 What is the longest-living animal?

7 Can it live up to 120 years, 135 or 180 years?

8 The fossa is a cat-like hunter which only lives on which African island?

9 What sort of creature was a New Zealand moa?

10 What is the name given to the female part of a creature which produces eggs?

Answers

1. Soil 2. It no longer exists 3. Talon 4. Colt 5. Bull 6. The giant tortoise 7. 180 years 8. Madagascar 9. A bird 10. The ovary

Quiz 4

1   How many arms does an octopus have?

2   What type of creature comes in varieties called hammerhead and great white?

3   How many years can a lion live to: 12, 20 or 30?

4   Are mammals warm- or cold-blooded?

5   Which cuddly Australian creature lives only on eucalyptus leaves?

6   Do conifers produce flowers?

7   What substance transports oxygen and nutrients around the human body?

8   What is a baby deer called?

9   Do all insects lay eggs?

10 What is the name given to an elephant's long pointed teeth?

Answers

1. Eight 2. The shark 3. 30 4. Warm-blooded 5. The koala 6. No 7. Blood 8. A fawn 9. Yes 10. Tusks

Clever Clogs

1　Are a hundredth, a fiftieth or a quarter of all the world's plants endangered?

2　What name is given to a female horse under the age of four?

3　Would you find gorillas in Africa, Europe, Asia or in all three?

4　What sort of creature is an ocelot?

5　What part of the human body secretes saliva?

6　What common name is often given to the sternum bone in humans?

7　Is a lobelia a plant, an insect or a virus?

8　What creature carries the disease malaria?

9　What name is given to the art of growing miniature trees and shrubs?

10　What is the outer covering of a tree's trunk called?

Answers

9. Bonsai 10. Bark

1. A quarter 2. Filly 3. Africa 4. A cat 5. The salivary gland 6. Breast bone 7. A plant 8. Mosquito

Quiz 6

1 The goldcrest bird holds what British record?

2 Does the spruce tree produce hardwood or softwood?

3 Where does a hamster carry grain and seeds?

4 What sort of creature is a natterjack?

5 What does an omnivore eat?

6 Are humans omnivores?

7 What is a young kangaroo called?

8 Where does an amphibian live?

9 What does a rhinoceros use its single horn for?

10 What part of the human body acts as a powerful pump?

Answers

7. A joey 8. In water and on land 9. Self defence 10. The heart

1. It is the smallest British bird 2. Softwood 3. In its cheeks 4. A toad 5. Plants and meat 6. Yes

164

Quiz 7

1 What African creature is related to the horse and has distinctive black and white striped markings?

2 Which country is the natural home of the Tasmanian devil?

3 What's the name of the fringe of hair that runs down a horse's neck?

4 What type of animal are Friesian and Jersey?

5 A peregrine falcon can reach 290 km/h in a dive — true or false?

6 What part of our bodies holds air when we breathe?

7 What part of a cow is squeezed to release milk?

8 How many kidneys does the human body normally contain?

9 What name is given to a fox's tail?

10 Arteries carry what from the heart?

Answers

Quiz 8

1 Which is the largest member of the cat family?

2 What white bird is considered the "bird of peace"?

3 Does the bulb of an onion grow below or above ground?

4 When is a nocturnal animal at its busiest?

5 What part of a plant takes in water?

6 Which is larger — the alligator or the crocodile?

7 What is the only poisonous snake found in Britain?

8 How many livers does the human body have?

9 Gorillas stick their tongues out to show anger — true or false?

10 What period of inactivity in winter do many mammals, including hedgehogs, go into?

Answers

1. The tiger 2. Dove 3. Below ground 4. At night 5. Its roots 6. The crocodile 7. The adder (or viper) 8. One 9. True 10. Hibernation

1 Which part of a rhubarb plant is poisonous?

2 What body part do fishes breathe through?

3 What does an invertebrate not have?

4 What substance makes leaves green?

5 Which animal has the heaviest brain: a sperm whale, a human or an elephant?

6 Entomologists study skin, insects or flowering plants?

7 What is a baby elephant called?

8 In which continent would you find alligators?

9 How does a python kill its prey?

10 Do cucumbers grow below or above ground?

Answers

1. Its leaves 2. Gills 3. A backbone 4. Chlorophyll 5. A sperm whale 6. Insects 7. Calf 8. North America 9. It crushes them 10. Above ground

Quiz 10

1 Penguins are only found in one continent; which is it?

2 Where is a rattlesnake's rattle?

3 In which continent would you find giant pandas and the snow leopard?

4 What type of animal are spaniels and beagles?

5 What are the two types of squirrel which live in Britain?

6 Can an emu fly?

7 Where do veins carry blood back to?

8 In which continent would you find llamas?

9 Do olives grow under the ground, on trees or on small flowering plants?

10 What tree provides conkers in autumn?

Answers

1. Antarctica 2. In its tail 3. Asia 4. Dogs 5. Red and grey squirrel 6. No 7. The heart 8. South America 9. On trees 10. Horse chestnut

Quiz 11

1 What is the world's largest bird?

2 How tall can an adult giraffe stand: 2.5 m, 3.5 m or 5.5 m?

3 What type of creature comes in varieties including fruit and vampire?

4 What is the scientific name for the large intestine?

5 Which is the largest penguin; the blue, the Adélie or the Emperor?

6 Is a chimpanzee a primate?

7 How many humps does a dromedary camel have?

8 Can a sea cucumber move?

9 Is the tail fin of a fish called the caudal fin, the dorsal fin or the pelvic fin?

10 Are knee joints hinge, ball and socket or sliding joints?

Answers

1. The ostrich 2. 5.5m 3. Bat 4. Colon 5. Emperor penguin 6. Yes 7. One 8. Yes, it can slide along the sea floor 9. Caudal fin 10. Hinge joints

Quiz 12

Whiz Kids

1 Which ape is covered in reddish fur and has very long limbs to swing through trees?

2 What pet is a domesticated form of the South American cavy?

3 Where in your body would you find metacarpal bones?

4 What does the pitcher plant eat?

5 In what part of your body would you find the cochlea and three semi-circular canals?

6 How many legs does a lobster have?

7 What is the human body's largest organ?

8 What creature has the largest eye in the animal kingdom?

9 Is that eye 13 cm, 37 cm or 52 cm in diameter?

10 Is the tamarisk: a tree, an insect or a small monkey?

Answers

1. Orang-utan 2. Guinea pig 3. Hands 4. Insects 5. The ear 6. Ten 7. The skin 8. Giant squid 9. 37 cm 10. A tree

Quiz 13

1 How many legs does a tapir have?

2 What is the only native British tree with a name starting with O?

3 What is a young pig called?

4 How long can a cockroach live without a head: one minute, one hour, one day or one week?

5 What type of dog is associated with the Queen?

6 The cabbage family of plants includes broccoli and radishes — true or false?

7 What is the full name of the popular bird pet the budgie?

8 How many arms does a starfish normally have?

9 What is a male cow called?

10 How many bones are there in a human neck: seven, 17 or 70?

Answers

1. Four 2. Oak 3. Piglet 4. One week 5. Corgi 6. True 7. Budgerigar 8. Five 9. Bull 10. Seven

Quiz 14

1 In which part of the body is waste stored before being pushed out of the anus?

2 Which bird has the biggest wingspan?

3 Is the mouse deer of Asia a real deer or not?

4 How tall does it grow: 25 cm, 1 m or 1.5 m high?

5 Does the male or female peacock have an incredible set of tail feathers?

6 How much food can an adult hippo eat overnight: 1 kg, 10 kg or 100 kg?

7 Is bamboo a tree or a grass?

8 Is an echidna a lizard, a small mammal or a type of beetle?

9 What measurement is used for the height of horses?

10 What vegetable did Mark Twain describe as a "cabbage with a college education"?

Answers

1. Rectum 2. The albatross 3. It is a real deer 4. 25cm high 5. The male peacock 6. 100 kg 7. A grass 8. A small mammal 9. Hands 10. Cauliflower

1 How many humps does a Bactrian camel have?

2 What are camels' humps used for?

3 Is the male part of a flower called a stigma, ovule or stamen?

4 How many kilos of plants can an adult elephant eat in a day?

5 How is an ocelot's coat patterned?

6 What type of creature is a Portuguese man-of-war?

7 What can a chameleon do with its eyes which most animals cannot?

8 What part of their bodies do hippos use to pluck grass out of the ground?

9 Are avocados fruit or vegetables?

10 Which two countries boast different species of echidna?

Answers

1. Two 2. As a fat store 3. Stamen 4. 110kg 5. With spots 6. A jellyfish 7. Move them in different directions at the same time. 8. Their lips 9. Fruit 10. Australia and New Zealand

Quiz 16

1 Which bird comes in the varieties tawny and barn?

2 How many leaves does a lucky clover have?

3 Do wild gerbils live in deserts, forests or on the African plains?

4 Do hippos eat fish?

5 Does a giraffe have more, less or the same number of neck bones as humans?

6 What is a female lion called?

7 Which bird lays the largest eggs?

8 What is a young bear called?

9 What colour do stoats turn in winter?

10 What is an anaconda?

Answers

1. Owl 2. Four 3. Deserts 4. No 5. The same number 6. Lioness 7. Ostrich 8. A cub 9. White 10. A snake

Quiz 17

1 Which is the slowest: a domestic cat, an elephant or a squirrel?

2 What other name is often give to the aubergine?

3 Do leopards mainly hunt at night or during the day?

4 Which is the fastest: a black mamba snake, a chicken or a pig?

5 How much water can a male giraffe drink in a day: 4 litres, 14 litres, 20 litres or 48 litres?

6 As a fraction, how much of the human body is made up of water?

7 Is a persimmon a fruit, an insect, a vegetable or a lizard?

8 What season do estivating animals sleep through?

9 What are roe?

10 What is a Venus flytrap?

Answers

9. The eggs of fish 10. A fly-eating plant

1. A squirrel 2. Eggplant 3. At night 4. A black mamba snake 5. 48 litres 6. $^2/_3$ 7. A fruit 8. Summer

Quiz 18

1 Which is the fastest: a grizzly bear, a human or a giraffe?

2 How long, in months, is the pregnancy of a white rhino?

3 What is the proper term for a young wolf?

4 Which food is botanically a fruit although it is commercially termed a vegetable?

5 Which monkey is a favoured prey of the leopard?

6 Apart from man, name one of the two natural enemies of hippos?

7 What is the name used for a male swan?

8 How many giant pandas exist: 1,000, 10,000 or 100,000?

9 Three quarters of the dust in a typical home consists of what?

10 Which is the longest bone in the human body?

Answers

1. A giraffe 2. 18 3. Pup 4. Tomato 5. Baboon 6. Lions and crocodiles 7. Cob 8. 1,000 9. Dead skin cells 10. The thigh bone or femur

Quiz 19

1 What are Basmati and Patna forms of?

2 Is a jaguar a member of the cat or dog family?

3 In which continent would you find jaguars?

4 What other Australian animal is the wallaby closely related to?

5 From which animal do we get the meats ham and bacon?

6 What typical cat feature is missing from the Manx cat?

7 Which is the world's biggest shark: the whale shark, the great white shark or the tiger shark?

8 What kind of creature are red admiral and cabbage white?

9 What is the nest where bees make honey called?

10 What fruit is used to make wine?

Answers

9. A hive 10. Grapes

1. Rice 2. Cat family 3. North America 4. Kangaroo 5. Pig 6. A tail 7. The whale shark 8. Butterflies

Quiz 20

Clever Clogs

1 What is another name for the trachea?

2 Does the male or female mosquito actually bite people?

3 What do bees collect from flowers to help make honey?

4 Is a peccary a wild pig, an insect collection or a small flowering bush?

5 What type of creature do ospreys eat?

6 How many milk teeth does a human have as a child?

7 And how many adult teeth are the milk teeth replaced with?

8 Are there over 1,000, over 600 or over 250 muscles in the human body?

9 How are the seeds of a dandelion dispersed?

10 Are spiders or fruit flies part of the arachnid family?

Answers

1. The windpipe 2. Female mosquito 3. Nectar 4. A wild pig 5. Fish 6. 20 7. 32 8. Over 600 9. By wind 10. Spiders

QUIZ 21

1. What name is given to a flower which needs to be planted every year?

2. What word describes a female swan?

3. How tall can a giant sunflower grow to: one, three or eight metres?

4. What is the largest artery travelling from the human heart called?

5. What salad vegetable was for many years considered poisonous?

6. The world consumption of what household product uses 29,160 hectares of woodland every day?

7. Dendochronology is the study of what part of a tree?

8. How long does a honey bee live for: six weeks, six months or six years?

9. The milk of which female farm animal is used to make feta cheese?

10. The chicle tree's sap is used to make what popular product?

ANSWERS

1. Annual 2. Pen 3. Three metres 4. Aorta 5. Tomato 6. Toilet paper 7. The rings in a tree's trunk 8. Six weeks 9. Sheep 10. Chewing gum

Quiz 22

1 How many wings does a bee have: two, four or six?

2 What mammal feeds entirely on ants?

3 Do insects have more or less legs than spiders?

4 If someone was examining your cranium, what part of your body would they be looking at?

5 Which creature boasts the biggest ears in the world?

6 Is a cygnet a young goose, duck or swan?

7 Is the chihuahua the smallest breed of dog?

8 Which is the only mammal that can fly?

9 Haricot, mung and butter are all types of what?

10 What are the fruits of an oak tree called?

Answers

1. Four 2. Anteater 3. Less 4. Head 5. African elephant 6. Swan 7. Yes 8. The bat 9. Bean 10. Acorns

Quiz 23

True or false?

1 The tarantula is the most poisonous spider?

2 Rhinos are placid creatures with poor eyesight?

3 Bald-headed eagles do have bald heads?

4 Dolphins sleep at night just below the surface of the water?

5 Lions will attack hippos?

6 Capsicum is another word for black peppercorns?

7 No two zebras have the same pattern of stripes?

8 Warthogs can run at speeds of 50 km/h?

9 Owls can turn their heads through 360 degrees?

10 Ostriches bury their heads in the sand when scared?

Answers

1. False 2. True 3. False 4. True 5. True 6. False 7. False 8. True 9. False 10. False

Quiz 24

True or false?

1 The duck-billed platypus is the only mammal to lay eggs?

2 Leopards will attack elephants?

3 When a baby kangaroo is born it is no bigger than a human thumb?

4 Lynx is another name for mountain lion?

5 Male mouth-brooding frogs carry the eggs of their young in vocal sacs?

6 The potato is closely related to the tomato and the bell pepper?

7 Ostriches are capable of digesting rocks and dirt?

8 A group of kangaroos are called a mob?

9 The meat veal comes from sheep?

10 A jellyfish is 95% water?

Answers

1. False 2. False 3. True 4. False 5. True 6. True 7. True 8. True 9. False 10. True

Quiz 25

True or false?

1　Brussels sprouts are miniature cabbages?

2　15,000 species of living thing are becoming extinct every year?

3　The cheetah can run at speeds of over 100 km/h?

4　Ostriches are today bred for their meat?

5　A domesticated otter is called a polecat?

6　Lettuce was considered a weed by the Romans?

7　The water vole is the smallest mammal in Britain?

8　Carrots belong to the parsley family?

9　The meat of a rabbit is called venison?

10　Basil is a herb related to mint?

Answers

1. False 2. True 3. True 4. True 5. False 6. True 7. False 8. True 9. False 10. True

Quiz 26

1 Do echidnas lay eggs?

2 How many legs does a crab have?

3 How many million times does your heart beat in a year?

4 What part of a chameleon is as long as its body?

5 Dogs can make around 10 distinctive sounds. How many more can a cat make?

6 What kind of tree do catkins grow on?

7 Is an anteater an African or South American animal?

8 What colour is the flower on the common poppy?

9 Is a leech a type of worm, scorpion or fly?

10 In which organ in the human body would you find the stirrup and anvil bones?

Answers

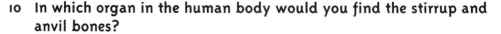

1. Yes 2. Ten 3. 37 million 4. Its tongue 5. More than 90 more (over 100 in all) 6. Hazel 7. South American 8. Red 9. Worm 10. The ear

1 What is the largest living thing on Earth?

2 How many litres of blood does an adult human body contain?

3 What domesticated animal is descended from Felis silvestris?

4 What is *Rafflesia arnoldi* the largest example of in the world?

5 In which Asian country would you find it?

6 In which river would you find the biggest crocodiles of all?

7 How many metres long can they grow to?

8 Dian Fossey is associated with the study and conservation of which animal?

9 Do hippos have tusks?

10 The narwhal has a spike protruding from its head. What is it made of?

Answers

10. Ivory

1. A tree (the sequoia) 2. Five 3. The cat 4. Flower 5. Indonesia 6. The Nile 7. Six 8. Gorillas 9. Yes

Quiz 28

1 How many toes does a hippo have on each hoof?

2 What is a female fox called?

3 What animal are Siamese and Burmese breeds of?

4 The meat of which animal provides T-bone and sirloin steaks?

5 Soya is used as a well-known meat substitute, but what sort of living thing is soya?

6 The giant kelp is the longest example of what marine plant?

7 What name is given to a male chicken?

8 Name any one of three native British trees beginning with the letter A?

9 What tree or bush has bright red berries and spiked leaves and is associated with Christmas?

10 Is a perch a freshwater or saltwater fish?

Answers

1. Four 2. Vixen 3. Cat 4. Cow 5. A bean 6. Seaweed 7. Rooster 8. Ash, alder or aspen 9. Holly 10. Freshwater

1　Hippos have been responsible for killing more than 400 people in Africa — true or false?

2　How much of the day do koalas sleep: two hours, four hours, 12 hours or 18 hours?

3　Which is the only big cat which lives in social groups?

4　How many stomachs does a camel have?

5　The duck-billed platypus is the only mammal which is poisonous — true or false?

6　What are your incisor teeth used for?

7　What colour is the blood of squid and octopuses?

8　The jelly-like substance in some bones has the same name as a type of large vegetable; what is it?

9　What name is given to trees which bear cones?

10　What bird builds an eyrie as a nest?

Answers

1. True 2. 18 hours 3. The lion 4. Four 5. True 6. Cutting food 7. Blue 8. Marrow 9. Conifers 10. Eagle

Quiz 30

1 The petals of the world's largest flower measure 20 cm, 30 cm or 50 cm across?

2 What is the world's largest land predator?

3 To the nearest 50 kg, how much can an adult male of this species weigh?

4 Can a narwhal's spike grow to one, two or three metres in length?

5 What are your molar teeth used for?

6 What sea creature with a sting has no heart or brain?

7 How do squid move through the water: jet propulsion, swimming with their tentacles or drifting with the water flow?

8 What do most white blood cells do in the human body?

9 Is balsa classified as a softwood or hardwood?

10 What part of sorrel do humans eat?

Answers

7. Jet propulsion 8. Fight germs 9. Hardwood 10. The leaves
1. 50 cm 2. The polar bear 3. 650 kg 4. Three metres 5. Grinding food up 6. Jellyfish

Quiz 31

1. Truffles are a form of fungi — name a more well-known edible fungi beginning with M?

2. What is a male duck called?

3. What creature creates natural silk?

4. Is a roach a freshwater or saltwater fish?

5. What word describes a female tiger?

6. What vegetable can make us cry when we peel and cut it?

7. What type of animal comes in the forms grey, humpback and sperm?

8. How many different species of elephant are there?

9. What are the two main ingredients of mayonnaise?

10. What creature can contain a natural pearl inside its shell?

Answers

1. Mushroom 2. Drake 3. Silkworm 4. Freshwater 5. Tigress 6. Onion 7. Whale 8. Two 9. Eggs (egg yolks) and oil 10. An oyster

Quiz 32

1 The Scots pine is the most commonly used tree in Britain for what purpose?

2 A jack ass is a male ass; what is a female called?

3 Is a banyan: a type of antelope, a tree or a small insect?

4 Do truffles grow above or below ground?

5 The deadly funnel-web spider is found in which country?

6 What word is used to describe a male rabbit?

7 What is unusual about the seeds of a strawberry?

8 Are frogs and newts amphibians?

9 What organ filters blood, removing water and other molecules in the human body?

10 The Arctic tern holds what bird record?

Answers

1. As a Christmas tree 2. Jenny 3. A tree 4. Below ground 5. Australia 6. Buck 7. They grow on the outside of the fruit 8. Yes 9. Kidneys 10. Longest bird migration

QUIZ 33

Whiz Kids

1. What is the largest creature in the world without a backbone?

2. 70% of all animals have three body parts and three sets of legs — what are they?

3. What type of teeth does an adult human have a maximum of four of?

4. What word describes any technique of preventing human fertilization?

5. Queen termites hold what insect record?

6. What part of many plants is concerned with reproduction?

7. What is the middle part of an insect's body called?

8. The spine-tailed swift is the world's fastest bird in level flight. How fast can it travel?

9. How many months does an elephant spend inside the mother before being born: 8–10, 14–16, 20–22 or 30–32?

10. Is the average life span of an ostrich longer than a lion?

Answers

1. Giant squid 2. Insects 3. Canines or wisdom 4. Contraception 5. Longest living 6. The flower 7. Thorax 8. 170 km/h 9. 20–22 months 10. Yes

Quiz 34

1 Colorado and death watch are types of which creature?

2 What is the name of a rabbit's burrow?

3 Is a mandrill: a parrot, a monkey or an insect?

4 What happens to a deciduous tree in Autumn?

5 Does the polar bear live in the Arctic or Antarctic?

6 Sloths go to the toilet: once a day, once every three days or once a week?

7 What name is given to a female dog?

8 Is a halibut a saltwater or freshwater fish?

9 Two thirds of a shark's brain is devoted to which sense?

10 Where would you find your Achilles tendon?

Answers

1. Beetle 2. A warren 3. A monkey 4. Its leaves fall off 5. The Arctic 6. Once a week 7. Bitch 8. Saltwater 9. Smell 10. On the heel of your foot.

Quiz 35

1 What part of your tongue can taste sweet things?

2 What is a baby goose called?

3 What British bird is an electric blue colour and is famous for its sudden dives into rivers?

4 The insect, called a midge, beats its wings 62, 620 or 62,000 times a minute?

5 What is the main food of the giant panda?

6 What kind of animal is a Gloucester Old Spot?

7 Do sharks ever eat their own young?

8 Wombats are only found on which island off Australia?

9 Can dingoes bark?

10 Does the boxwood tree produce hardwood or softwood?

Answers

1. The front tip 2. Gosling 3. Kingfisher 4. 62,000 5. Bamboo shoots 6. A pig 7. Yes, sometimes 8. Tasmania 9. No 10. Hardwood

Quiz 36

1 An elephant's trunk contains 40,000 muscles — true or false?

2 Which North American animal is the largest member of the deer family?

3 What word, beginning with B, means relating to the cow or buffalo?

4 What is a male bee without a sting called?

5 Belladonna is another name for which poisonous British plant?

6 What two animals are crossed to form a mule?

7 How many claws facing forward and how many backward does a parrot have?

8 Where would you find heartwood in a tree?

9 Does the pygmy shark, which grows just 20cm long, exist?

10 How far can grey kangaroos jump in a single bound: six, nine, 14 or 30 metres?

Answers

1. True 2. Moose 3. Bovine 4. A drone 5. Deadly nightshade 6. A horse and a donkey 7. Two forward and two backward 8. In the centre of the tree's trunk 9. Yes 10. 14 metres

Easy Peasy

1 Mayflies live for just two hours – true or false?

2 Are birds warm or cold-blooded?

3 Topiary is the art of clipping what into fancy shapes?

4 Do slugs have one, four or fifty noses?

5 What sort of creature is an anaconda?

6 On what part of your body are your taste buds?

7 Can a hummingbird fly backwards as well as forwards?

8 Does food travel through your stomach or large intestine first?

9 Where would you find a clavicle bone: your shoulder, your foot or your wrist?

10 Are tulips grown from seed or bulbs?

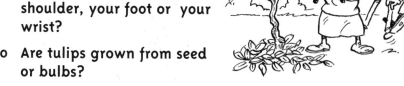

WELL, HOW DO YOU THINK IT LOOKS?

Answers

1. True 2. Warm-blooded 3. Hedges and trees 4. Four! 5. A snake 6. Your tongue 7. Yes 8. Stomach 9. Your shoulder 10. Bulbs

People

Here are 37 quizzes to test your knowledge of famous people. They include questions on people in history such as national heroes and leaders, writers and painters. There are also plenty of questions on people alive today.

The quizzes are divided into three levels of difficulty: Easy Peasy, Clever Clogs and Whiz Kids. As you can probably guess Easy Peasy are the easiest, Clever Clogs the next most difficult and Whiz Kids the hardest. However, the easiest questions are always the ones where you know the answers!

Good luck.

Quiz 1

1 What is the first name of Tony Blair's wife?

2 Which silent film actor played the part of the little tramp?

3 What country was Adolf Hitler born in?

4 Was Marilyn Monroe a singer, actress or painter?

5 In which military force did Douglas Bader fight?

6 In the Bible, who led the animals in "two by two"?

7 Harry Webb is the real name of which long-running pop singer?

8 Which wartime prime minister had the nickname "Winnie"?

9 What was the first name of Hardy, of Laurel and Hardy fame?

10 What nationality was Leonardo da Vinci?

Answers

1. Cherie 2. Charlie Chaplin 3. Austria 4. Actress 5. The RAF 6. Noah 7. Cliff Richard 8. Winston Churchill 9. Oliver 10. Italian

Quiz 2

Clever Clogs

1　Which British boxer fought Mike Tyson in Manchester in January 2000?

2　Is Tom O'Connor a comedian, a singer or a professional golfer?

3　In what job has David Lean achieved fame?

4　Which painter's most famous work is *The Haywain*?

5　Which singer-songwriter once used to be in the pop duo Wham!?

6　What outstanding facial feature did Cyrano de Bergerac have?

7　Which American comedian played an updated version of Cyrano in the film *Roxanne*?

8　For what did Philip Larkin become famous?

9　Which famous Tudor explorer wrote a history of the world whilst imprisoned in the Tower of London?

10　Which female criminal was found guilty of the Moors Murders?

Answers

7. Steve Martin 8. Poetry 9. Sir Walter Raleigh 10. Myra Hindley

1. Julius Francis 2. A comedian 3. Film directing 4. John Constable 5. George Michael 6. A huge nose

Quiz 3

1 Which president was romantically linked with Marilyn Monroe?

2 What were the surnames of the two English writers of comic operettas?

3 In Roman mythology, who was the messenger of the Gods?

4 Which former *Carry On* star has played the landlady of *EastEnders'* pub, The Queen Vic?

5 Who was the first person to fly solo across the Atlantic?

6 What was the name of his aircraft?

7 Who made over 1,000 inventions, including the phonograph and practical electric lighting?

8 Which country did he come from?

9 What is the real name of punk singer Johnny Rotten?

10 Which political party did Sir James Goldsmith form in 1994?

Answers

1. John F. Kennedy 2. Gilbert and Sullivan 3. Mercury 4. Barbara Windsor 5. Charles Lindbergh 6. *Spirit of St Louis* 7. Thomas Edison 8. The United States 9. John Lydon 10. The Referendum Party

Quiz 4

1 Who owns the Virgin business empire?

2 In what sort of craft has he tried to make long distance voyages?

3 What was the first name of Laurel, of Laurel and Hardy fame?

4 Which country does the comedian Billy Connolly come from?

5 What did Glenda Jackson do before she became an MP?

6 Which political party does she represent?

7 Who painted the *Mona Lisa*?

8 Who is the patron saint of England?

9 Which figure in the Bible fought Goliath?

10 With what device did he fight?

Answers

1. Richard Branson 2. Balloon 3. Stan 4. Scotland 5. She was an actress 6. Labour Party 7. Leonardo da Vinci 8. St George 9. David 10. A slingshot

Quiz 5

1 Which actor and heart-throb played the male lead in *Titanic*?

2 Who was the actress and singer daughter of Judy Garland?

3 Which actor/director was Emma Thompson married to?

4 Who was Ronald Reagan's vice president?

5 Reg Dwight is the real name of which singer?

6 Which politician earned the nickname "The Iron Lady"?

7 Cherilyn Sarkisian shortened her name and became a famous singer; who is she?

8 What was the name of her husband and co-singer?

9 Fred Lasby was the oldest person to do what in an aircraft?

10 What nationality was Pablo Picasso?

Answers

1. Leonardo Di Caprio 2. Liza Minelli 3. Kenneth Branagh 4. George Bush 5. Elton John 6. Margaret Thatcher 7. Cher 8. Sonny Bono 9. Fly round the world 10. Spanish

Quiz 6

1 What does the F in John F. Kennedy's name stand for?

2 Who was the first bowler to take 300 Test wickets?

3 What type of drink does Oz Clark write about?

4 Who is the current editor of *Private Eye*?

5 On which long-running news quiz show does he appear?

6 What did King Alfred the Great allegedly burn?

7 Which king was murdered in Pontefract Castle?

8 Who is the patron saint of France: St Pierre, St Denis or St Michel?

9 Gertrude Ederle was the first woman to do what in 1926?

10 William Booth founded which "army"?

Answers

1. Fitzgerald 2. Fred Trueman 3. Wine 4. Ian Hislop 5. *Have I Got News For You* 6. The cakes 7. Richard II 8. St Denis 9. Swim the English Channel 10. The Salvation Army

Easy Peasy

1 What is the name of the host of *Supermarket Sweep* and other game shows?

2 Which tennis player has been romantically linked to Barbra Streisand?

3 Which action hero is actress Demi Moore married to?

4 What does Michael Fish do on television?

5 Which king was known as "The Lionheart"?

6 Who married Prince Edward in 1999?

7 Which composer wrote *The Four Seasons*?

8 For which sport did Michael Jordan become famous?

9 What was the surname of the singers Donny, Marie, Jay and Jimmy?

10 How many people attended Mozart's funeral: one, 40, 100 or 1,000?

Answers

1. Dale Winton 2. Andre Agassi 3. Bruce Willis 4. He's a weatherman 5. Richard 6. Sophie Rhys-Jones 7. Vivaldi 8. Basketball 9. Osmond 10. One

Quiz 8

1   Who is the patron saint of Wales?

2   What film saw the first acting performance of footballer Vinnie Jones?

3   Which British tennis player was Chris Evert once married to?

4   With what sort of vehicle is Barry Sheene associated?

5   Who was Prince Charles' best man at his wedding to Diana?

6   O.J. Simpson once played which sport professionally?

7   Which series of spoof detective films did he star in alongside Leslie Nielsen?

8   Which heavyweight boxer was once married to Robin Givens?

9   What popular sport was devised by James Naismith?

10 Who succeeded Edward VII after he abdicated?

Answers

1. St David 2. *Lock, Stock and Two Smoking Barrels* 3. John Lloyd 4. Motorcycles 5. He didn't have one 6. American football 7. *The Naked Gun* 8. Mike Tyson 9. Basketball 10. George VI

Quiz 9

1 Which film star's real name was Norma Jean Baker?

2 Which jazz singer and trumpeter was nicknamed Satchmo?

3 Which country did Ian Smith lead?

4 What has Ang Rita Sherpa done more times than any other person?

5 Which British prime minister said "You've never had it so good"?

6 The Rosetta Stone gave the key to Egyptian hieroglyphics. Where is it?

7 Which fashion designer has made clothes for Madonna and used to star on *Eurotrash*?

8 Which famous Hollywood star gave her name to a type of lifejacket?

9 What did the Russian dictator, Stalin, study at university?

10 Which Anita founded the Body Shop company?

Answers

10. Anita Roddick

5. Harold Macmillan 6. In the British Museum 7. Jean-Paul Gaultier 8. Mae West 9. Theology

1. Marilyn Monroe 2. Louis Armstrong 3. Rhodesia 4. Climbed Everest without oxygen

Quiz 10

1. Who wrote *The Planets* suite?
2. What nationality was he: German, Czech or British?
3. Was the Yorkshire Ripper a real person or a fictional character?
4. Of which company is Bill Gates the president?
5. Which gangster was nicknamed "Scarface"?
6. What did William Wilberforce fight to abolish?
7. Who was alleged to have said "We are not amused"?
8. With which instrument is Eric Clapton associated?
9. What was the painter Van Gogh's first name?
10. Which movie actor has the nickname "Sly"?

Answers

1. Gustav Holst 2. British 3. A real person 4. Microsoft 5. Al Capone 6. Slavery 7. Queen Victoria 8. Electric guitar 9. Vincent 10. Sylvester Stallone

1 Which European country had a leader by the name of King Zog?

2 Which famous movie star had the nickname "Duke"?

3 What bit Queen Elizabeth II in 1991?

4 With what campaign is the name Emily Pankhurst associated?

5 Which Southampton football player was appointed manager of Wales?

6 Which Hollywood film star became mayor of the town of Carmel?

7 How much was he paid per year for the job: $200, $2,000, $20,000 or $200,000?

8 Which singing star's real name is Annie Mae Bullock?

9 Who was woken in their bed in 1982 by intruder, Michael Fagan?

10 What did John Loudon McAdam improve?

Answers

1. Albania 2. John Wayne 3. One of her corgi dogs 4. Votes for women 5. Mark Hughes 6. Clint Eastwood 7. $200 8. Tina Turner 9. Queen Elizabeth II 10. Roads

Quiz 12

1 Was Frank Sinatra once married to Mia Farrow, Lulu or Cher?

2 Who was the inventor of the *Peanuts* cartoon strip?

3 Which international statesman received the Nobel Peace Prize in 1990?

4 What did Mary Read do for a living?

5 What was the profession of American, Frank Lloyd Wright?

6 Of which country was Archbishop Makarios the first president?

7 What nationality was Prince Henry the Navigator?

8 Which threatened author made a surprise appearance at a 1993 U2 concert?

9 What weapon was Sir Barnes Wallis famous for building?

10 In what year did Prince Charles and Diana marry?

Answers

1. Mia Farrow 2. Charles Schulz 3. Mikhail Gorbachev 4. She was a pirate 5. Architect 6. Cyprus 7. Portuguese 8. Salman Rushdie 9. A bouncing bomb 10. 1981

Quiz 13

1 What is "Sporty Spice", Mel C's real name?

2 Which Australian soap started the careers of Jason Donovan and Kylie Minogue?

3 Who was the man behind the cartoon characters Mickey Mouse and Donald Duck?

4 Which John has been Minister for Transport and is nicknamed "Two Jags"?

5 What nationality was the painter Claude Monet?

6 Was he: a cubist, an impressionist or a Renaissance artist?

7 Which famous singer-songwriter was born Robert Zimmerman?

8 In what year was Prince William of Wales born: 1973, 1976, 1982 or 1986?

9 Is he older or younger than his brother Harry?

10 The artist Frans Hals painted a famous picture of a cavalier — what was the cavalier doing?

Answers

1. Melanie Chisholm 2. *Neighbours* 3. Walt Disney 4. John Prescott 5. French 6. Impressionist 7. Bob Dylan 8. 1982 9. Older 10. Laughing

Quiz 14

1 Which Fascist leader of Italy was nicknamed Il Duce?

2 Which sports presenter transferred from BBC to ITV in 1999?

3 What kind of tax was William Pitt famous for introducing in 1799?

4 What were the Romans Virgil, Ovid and Horace?

5 "Thank God I have done my duty" were the last words of which naval war hero?

6 Which British 400 m runner was a BMX bike champion as a child?

7 Which millionaire ran for American president as an independent in 1992?

8 What was the name of the Yorkshire Ripper?

9 Who is now estimated to be the richest person in the world?

10 Which pop group of brothers who had hits with *ABC* and *One Bad Apple*, included Michael and Jermaine?

Answers

1. Mussolini 2. Des Lynam 3. Income tax 4. Poets 5. Lord Nelson 6. Iwan Thomas 7. Ross Perot 8. Peter Sutcliffe 9. Bill Gates 10. The Jacksons or Jackson Five

Whiz Kids

1 Which film director was Mia Farrow married to up until the 1990s?

2 In which Oscar-winning film did she appear, married to Michael Caine?

3 How much did Bill Gates buy the computer operating system Ms-DOS for: $75,000, $7.5 million or $75 million?

4 What artform is Barbara Hepworth known for?

5 Who shot and killed Lee Harvey Oswald?

6 The Neville brothers are famous footballers. What does their sister, Tracy, play for England?

7 What is the first name of the Neville brothers and sister's father?

8 Which Scottish actor received a knighthood in the 1999 New Year's Honours list?

9 Of which political party was Jeremy Thorpe once a leader?

10 Peach Melba got its name from which opera singer?

Answers

1. Woody Allen 2. *Hannah and her Sisters* 3. $75,000 4. Sculpture 5. Jack Ruby 6. Netball 7. Neville 8. Sean Connery 9. The Liberal Party 10. Dame Nellie Melba

Quiz 16

1 Which philosopher wrote *Das Kapital* which inspired many generations of communists?

2 What are both the Gibbs and Leslie pairs of brothers famous for playing?

3 Which artist of the 1960s and 1970s shortened his name from Andrew Warhola?

4 Which saint is Santa Claus named after?

5 Which ancient king had a round table?

6 Which religious leader lives in the Vatican City?

7 How many brothers does Princess Anne have?

8 Were the *"Two Fat Ladies"* cooks, book critics or travel show presenters?

9 Which Judy played Dorothy in the film version of *The Wizard of Oz*?

10 Was André Previn: a comedian, painter, violinist or conductor?

Answers

1. Karl Marx 2. Rugby union 3. Andy Warhol 4. St Nicholas 5. King Arthur 6. The Pope 7. Three 8. Cooks 9. Judy Garland 10. A conductor

Clever Clogs

1 Mohamed Al-Fayed owns which famous store?

2 Which jazz instrumentalist was known as "The Bird"?

3 Did he play the jazz guitar, the saxophone or the trumpet?

4 Who was the first wife of William Shakespeare?

5 How many middle names does Prince William have?

6 Which communist philosopher's dying words were: "Last words are for fools who haven't said enough"?

7 Which minister was disgraced in the Profumo Affair?

8 In what era did a figure called Jack the Ripper terrorise London?

9 Who was the musical *Evita* written about?

10 And in what country did she live?

Answers

1. Harrods 2. Charlie Parker 3. The saxophone 4. Anne Hathaway 5. Three 6. Karl Marx 7. John Profumo 8. The Victorian era 9. Eva Perón 10. Argentina

213

Quiz 18

1 Which king of England couldn't speak any English?

2 Which writer won the Pulitzer prize in 1952 for his book *The Old Man and the Sea*?

3 What was Margaret Bondfield the first woman to do in 1929?

4 Who was the only bachelor president of the United States?

5 Which Tory party member is a famous author and was running for Mayor of London?

6 Which countess is considered the world's first computer programmer?

7 Was the computer language FORTH, ADA or COBOL named in her honour?

8 Which two comedians starred on the *Fantasy Football League* TV show?

9 Which English middle-distance runner became a Conservative MP in the 1990s?

10 Which star of the films *Mona Lisa* and *Hannah and Her Sisters* was originally called Maurice Micklewhite?

Answers

9. Sebastian Coe 10. Michael Caine
5. Jeffrey Archer 6. Countess Ada Lovelace 7. ADA 8. David Baddiel and Frank Skinner
1. George I 2. Ernest Hemingway 3. Become the first female cabinet minister 4. James Buchanan

Quiz 19

1 What brothers flew their aeroplane from Kitty Hawk in 1903?

2 Which tough-guy actor had the nickname Bogey?

3 Which famous pop drummer's real name is Richard Starkey?

4 With which classical musical instrument is Nigel Kennedy associated?

5 Jim Henson provided the puppets for which famous children's show?

6 Which sisters were responsible for classics of English literature including *Wuthering Heights*?

7 What standard facial feature is missing from the *Mona Lisa* painting?

8 What is Sean Connery's real first name: Titus, Thomas or Timothy?

9 Which group of brothers would you be watching if you could see Harpo, Zeppo and Groucho?

10 Was Carlos the Jackal: a film character, a terrorist or an enemy of the Crusades?

Answers

7. Eyebrows 8. Thomas 9. The Marx Brothers 10. A terrorist

1. The Wright brothers 2. Humphrey Bogart 3. Ringo Starr 4. The violin 5. *The Muppets* 6. The Brontës

Quiz 20

1 Who invented the Baygen radio which requires no batteries?

2 Which winner of the 1996 Rugby World Cup received the trophy from Nelson Mandela?

3 In what band was Michael Hutchence the lead singer and songwriter?

4 Who was the girlfriend of Michael Hutchence at the time of his death?

5 And which Boomtown Rat had she been married to previously?

6 Name the actress/MP who was an early candidate in the election for the Mayor of London?

7 What have union leader Jimmy Hoffa, aviator Amelia Earhart and Lord Lucan all got in common?

8 Which actress was Humphrey Bogart married to?

9 What computing device did Douglas J. Englebart invent: the hard disk, the joystick, the mouse or the microprocessor?

10 Which two politicians contested the nomination as Labour Party candidate for the Mayor of London?

Answers

1. Trevor Baylis 2. François Pienaar 3. INXS 4. Paula Yates 5. Bob Geldof 6. Glenda Jackson 7. They all disappeared and have never been traced 8. Lauren Bacall 9. The mouse 10. Frank Dobson and Ken Livingstone

Quiz 21

1 Who wrote the novel *The Great Gatsby*?

2 Who was the first person to meet Christ after the crucifixion?

3 Which pianist and composer wrote *Maple Leaf Rag* and other ragtime songs?

4 Whose famous art studio in the 1960s was called The Factory?

5 Which cartoonist's first job was drawing pictures for a barber, receiving 25 US cents or a free haircut per picture?

6 Which Peter's biography, full of stories of his acting and writing days, was called *Just Me*?

7 Dashiell Hammett created which tough, fictional detective?

8 If your surname is Cooper, historically what would you have been?

9 If you were nicknamed "Dusty", what would your surname most likely be?

10 Which American male tennis player was known as "Superbrat" and "Motormouth"?

Answers

1. F. Scott Fitzgerald 2. Mary Magdalene 3. Scott Joplin 4. Andy Warhol 5. Walt Disney 6. Peter Ustinov 7. Sam Spade 8. A barrel maker 9. Miller 10. John McEnroe

Quiz 22

1 What is the nationality of snooker player Stephen Hendry?

2 How did flying ace Douglas Bader lose his legs?

3 What sport did he become very good at in later life?

4 With which sport would you associate father and son, Harry and Jamie Redknapp?

5 Soul singer Natalie Cole had an even more famous singing father with a similar name; what was it?

6 Which captain did Princess Anne marry in the 1970s?

7 What nationality is Jesse Jackson?

8 Has he ever run for president of the United States?

9 How much did the heaviest man in Britain Peter Yarnall, weigh when he died: 278 kg, 328 kg or 368 kg?

10 What did Sir Edmund Hillary climb?

Answers

1. Scottish 2. In a flying accident 3. Golf 4. Football 5. Nat King Cole 6. Mark Phillips 7. American 8. Yes 9. 368kg (58 stone) 10. Mount Everest

Quiz 23

1. What was the original name of boxer Muhammad Ali?
2. Who is the patron saint of Scotland?
3. How did Nirvana singer, Kurt Cobain, die?
4. Who was the wife of Kurt Cobain at the time of his death?
5. Which physicist, famous for his work on black holes, has motor neurone disease and is wheelchair-bound?
6. Which car maker once said, "History is bunk"?
7. Was O.J. Simpson found guilty or innocent of killing his wife?
8. Which German engineer, called Willy, gave his surname to a range of World War II aircraft?
9. Who owns *The Sun* and *The Times* newspapers?
10. Which Russian communist leader's name had the meaning "man of steel"?

Answers

1. Cassius Clay 2. St Andrew 3. He committed suicide 4. Courtney Love 5. Stephen Hawking 6. Henry Ford 7. Innocent 8. Messerschmitt 9. Rupert Murdoch 10. Stalin

Quiz 24

1 What did Howling Wolf and Big Mama Thornton become famous for?

2 Cameron MacIntosh is a famous: Australian politician, Scottish politician, theatre impresario or film director?

3 Which comic actor and wit owned *Private Eye* magazine until his death in 1995?

4 What was the name of the Manchester doctor found guilty of killing 15 patients?

5 Who is the patron saint of Ireland?

6 Which American political party does Newt Gingrich belong to?

7 Who plays Sir Les Patterson and Dame Edna Everage?

8 Which Australian supermodel has the nickname "The Body"?

9 Who was Elvis Presley's manager?

10 Who in a four year period made 300 inventions, one every five days?

Answers

1. Singing the blues 2. Theatre impresario 3. Peter Cook 4. Dr Harold Shipman 5. St Patrick 6. Republican 7. Barry Humphries 8. Elle Macpherson 9. Colonel Tom Parker 10. Thomas Edison

Quiz 25

1 In the Bible, what were the names of Adam's two sons?

2 Was Sir Christopher Wren: an architect, a British prime minister or a naval captain?

3 Who is the patron saint of travellers, an image of whom is often worn around the neck?

4 Henry Moore is known as a sculptor, a poet, a playwright or a painter?

5 Which US president was known as "Honest Abe"?

6 Who did Melinda, a product manager at Microsoft, marry in 1994?

7 Who is the heir to the British throne?

8 Which one of the following is not a current Labour MP: Neil Kinnock, Robin Cook, Harriet Harman, Jack Straw?

9 Who sentenced Jesus to death?

10 How was writer, Herbert George Wells, better known?

Answers

Quiz 26

1 Which film actress is married to Tom Cruise?

2 Which saint is commemorated on February 14?

3 Carl Sagan was noted for his work in which scientific field?

4 Which two Marks have a Radio One afternoon show?

5 Bill Gates' new house has how many garages: 3, 5, 9 or 35?

6 During the Gulf War, what was the nickname of military man, H.N. Schwarzkopf?

7 Painter Paul Gauguin lived and painted on which South Pacific island?

8 Which one of the following was not a member of Monty Python: Terry Jones, Terry Gilliam, Marty Feldman, Graham Chapman?

9 Who is the Princess Royal of England?

10 How old was Minie Monroe when she got married in 1991 to a man of 83?

Answers

1. Nicole Kidman 2. St Valentine 3. Planetary science 4. Mark Radcliffe and Mark Riley 5. 35 6. "Stormin' Norman" 7. Tahiti 8. Marty Feldman 9. Princess Anne 10. 103

Quiz 27

1. Is Tracy Emin: a soul singer, a choreographer or a modern artist?

2. Which actress is director Blake Edwards married to?

3. Which Australian media owner organized a rebel cricket competition?

4. Which Victorian engineer had the initials I.K.B.?

5. Which former Yorkshire batsman now gives expert cricket analysis on Talk Radio?

6. Matthew and John are two of the Gospels; can you name the other two?

7. Runner, Derek Redmond, is married to which famous swimmer?

8. What was the surname of the twins who terrorised the East End in the 1960s?

9. And which pair of brothers portrayed them on film?

10. Which ex-Beatle is a member of the Travelling Wilburys band?

Answers

1. A modern artist 2. Julie Andrews 3. Kerry Packer 4. Isambard Kingdom Brunel 5. Geoffrey Boycott 6. Luke and Mark 7. Sharron Davies 8. The Krays 9. The Kemps, Martin and Gary 10. George Harrison

Quiz 28

1 Which snooker player is nicknamed "The Whirlwind"?

2 If you were with Naomi, Claudia and Elle, would you most likely be at a fashion show, on a theatre stage or playing at a pop concert?

3 What was Mussolini's first name?

4 What is the name of Prince Andrew's eldest daughter: Zara, Eugenie or Beatrice?

5 Henry Matisse became famous as a classical composer, an opera singer or a painter?

6 Who was Frank James' more famous outlaw brother?

7 Which sport did Harry Carpenter commentate on for more than fifty years?

8 Which limb did Lord Nelson lose in battle?

9 John McCarthy and Terry Waite were held captive in which Middle Eastern country?

10 What was the first name of Nelson Mandela's first wife?

Answers

1. Jimmy White 2. A fashion show 3. Benito 4. Beatrice 5. A painter 6. Jesse James 7. Boxing 8. His right arm 9. Lebanon 10. Winnie

Quiz 29

1 Which motorcycle daredevil's real name was Robert Craig?

2 Who is the patron of the World Wide Fund for Nature?

3 Who is third in line to the British throne?

4 Which general ruled Spain until his death in 1975?

5 Which US president was nicknamed "Ike"?

6 Whose wealth is estimated at 48 billion dollars?

7 Which famous film actress has Warren Beatty as a brother?

8 Name either of the actress daughters of Sir Michael Redgrave?

9 Which Middle Eastern king married and divorced Toni Gardiner?

10 Who was Angelica Huston's famous film director father?

Answers

1. Evel Knievel 2. Prince Philip 3. Prince Harry 4. General Franco 5. Eisenhower 6. Bill Gates 7. Shirley Maclean 8. Vanessa and Lynn 9. King Hussein of Jordan 10. John Huston

Quiz 30

1 By what name is Gordon Sumner better known?

2 Who was the Greek slave who wrote a collection of fables?

3 Who is the patron saint of doctors?

4 How old was Daisy Ashford when she wrote *The Young Visiters*: nine, 14, 19 or 90?

5 What name, beginning with S, was given to the work of artists such as Salvador Dali and René Magritte?

6 Sir Stamford Raffles founded a trading post in which South East Asian country?

7 Which Australian feminist wrote *The Female Eunuch*?

8 Which actress, with the original name Joyce Frankenberg, changed her name to the same as one of Henry VIII's wives?

9 What did Lord Nelson lose the use of at the Siege of Calvi in 1794?

10 Who is seventh in line to the British throne?

Answers

1. Sting 2. Aesop 3. St Luke 4. Nine 5. Surrealism 6. Singapore 7. Germaine Greer 8. Jane Seymour 9. His right eye 10. Prince Edward

Quiz 31

Easy Peasy

1 Which band were nicknamed the "Fab Four"?

2 Did Gene Hackman, Gene Kelly or Gene Wilder play Popeye Doyle in the *French Connection* films?

3 With what entertainment has Prince Edward been associated with?

4 How many children does Princess Anne have?

5 Which former prime minister has two children, Carol and Mark?

6 What is the first name of Bill and Hillary Clinton's daughter?

7 Which English general gave his name to a type of rubber boot?

8 Actor Tony Booth is the father of which politician's wife?

9 Which wife of King Henry VIII is said to have had six fingers on one hand?

10 Tom Selleck turned down which role in the adventure series of films starting with a Lost Ark?

Answers

1. The Beatles 2. Gene Hackman 3. Theatre 4. Two 5. Margaret Thatcher 6. Chelsea 7. Duke of Wellington 8. Tony Blair 9. Anne Boleyn 10. Indiana Jones

227

Quiz 32

1 Who is W.A.P.L. Windsor better known as?

2 Which ex-Labour leader has a wife called Glennis?

3 What is the surname of the brothers, one a natural history film-maker, the other an actor and director of films such as *Gandhi*?

4 In 1991, what notable British first did Helen Sharman achieve?

5 For what crime was gangster Al Capone eventually imprisoned?

6 Which British queen was nicknamed "Good Queen Bess"?

7 Which Conservative Party politician was released from jail in January 2000, wearing an electronic tag?

8 What fear or phobia did both Marilyn Monroe and Howard Hughes have?

9 What did Sir Rowland Hill pioneer in Victorian times?

10 Which fighter pilot's life was portrayed in the film *Reach for the Sky?*

Answers

1. Prince William 2. Neil Kinnock 3. David and Richard Attenborough 4. She was the first British woman in space 5. Income tax evasion 6. Elizabeth I 7. Jonathan Aitken 8. Agoraphobia – fear of open spaces 9. The penny post using postage stamps 10. Douglas Bader

Whiz Kids

1 Which religious leader's real name is Karol Jozef Wojtyla?

2 Which film, with the lead played by John Hurt, was about the real life of John Merrick?

3 Which member of *Beyond the Fringe* is a medical doctor: Peter Cook, Alan Bennett or Jonathan Miller?

4 Who was the first woman to fly solo from England to Australia?

5 What did John Paul Getty III lose when kidnapped in 1974?

6 Which horse-racing commentator retired in 1997 after fifty years service?

7 Which actress has won a record four Oscars in major roles?

8 Which English king was known as "The Unready"?

9 In which European country do people not have surnames?

10 Who founded the Boy Scouts?

Answers

1. Pope John Paul II 2. *The Elephant Man* 3. Jonathan Miller 4. Amy Johnson 5. His right ear 6. Peter O'Sullivan 7. Katharine Hepburn 8. Ethelred 9. Iceland 10. Sir Robert Baden-Powell

229

Quiz 34

1　Was the composer Frederic Chopin: English, French, Italian or Polish?

2　Which Paulo pushed a football referee over: Di Canio, Maldini or Wanchope?

3　Thor Heyerdahl sailed on a raft from Polynesia to which country: Peru, Australia or the United States?

4　By what nickname is Emma Bunton better known?

5　Who wrote the music for the *Lion King*: George Michael, Steps, Andrew Lloyd-Webber or Elton John?

6　Which balding British chat show host is a fully trained and practising lawyer?

7　Jacques Cousteau is associated with what sort of exploration: undersea, mountain, space or jungle?

8　Stanley Gibbons was a dealer in what collectable item?

9　Which pop star did Mark Chapman shoot dead in 1980?

10　Which artist was married to the pop star in question nine?

Answers

1. Polish 2. Paulo Di Canio 3. Peru 4. Baby Spice 5. Elton John 6. Clive Anderson 7. Undersea 8. Stamps 9. John Lennon 10. Yoko Ono

Quiz 35

Clever Clogs

1 Which singer and drummer played the Artful Dodger as a child actor?

2 What do actress Susan Hampshire, writer Hans Christian Andersen and General Patton all have in common?

3 Which US president bought Louisiana from France?

4 By what nickname was Wild West outlaw William Bonney better known?

5 Lady Emma Hamilton caused a stir by having a romantic attachment to which war hero?

6 What was Sir Henry Cole the first to do at Christmas in 1843?

7 What first name, which rhymes with his surname, did David Bowie give to his son?

8 Which former England football manager co-wrote the *Hazel* detective series?

9 Who was the BBC Sports Personality of the Year, 2001?

10 Which American president gave his name to the teddy bear?

Answers

1. Phil Collins 2. They are or were all dyslexic 3. Thomas Jefferson 4. Billy the Kid 5. Nelson 6. Send Christmas cards 7. Zowie 8. Terry Venables 9. David Beckham 10. Theodore Roosevelt

Quiz 36

1 Which former news reporter contested and won a seat in Parliament standing as an independent?

2 Which Conservative politician did he defeat at the election?

3 Which jazz singer was known as Lady Day?

4 Who pioneered effective treatments against anthrax and rabies?

5 Malcolm Little changed his surname to include just one letter; what was it?

6 Who was the youngest ever British prime minister?

7 Who made his money in sugar and financed a famous art gallery in London?

8 Who were Pavlova, Nijinsky and Fonteyn?

9 Which inventor created the three-wheeled electric car after a series of ZX home computers?

10 Who directed the films *ET, The Color Purple* and *Jaws*?

Answers

1. Martin Bell 2. Neil Hamilton 3. Billie Holliday 4. Louis Pasteur 5. Malcolm X 6. William Pitt the Younger 7. Sir Henry Tate 8. Ballet dancers 9. Sir Clive Sinclair 10. Steven Spielberg

Quiz 37

1 Arthur Scargill was a union leader in which industry: coal mining, shipping or teaching?

2 Oswald Mosley was the leader of British Union of Fascists or the British Communist Party in the 1930's??

3 Was William the Conqueror a Roman, a Saxon or a Norman?

4 Which football team has Micael Owen played for all of his career, so far?

5 Are Lee Hurst and Jack Dee: tap dancers, comedians or newsreaders?

6 Did Mae West, Sophia Loren or Madonna give her name to a type of life-jacket?

7 Is Karl Marx buried in Britain, France or Germany?

8 Was Ian Dury a sculptor, a pop musician or a theatre director?

9 What nationality is the actor Jude Law?

10 How many Oscars has Michael Caine won: none, one or two?

Answers

1. Coal mining 2. British Union of Fascists 3. A Norman 4. Liverpool 5. Comedians 6. Mae West 7. Britain 8. Pop musician 9. British 10. Two

History

Here are 37 quizzes to test your knowledge of history – its people, battles, inventions and major events.

The quizzes are divided into three levels of difficulty: Easy Peasy, Clever Clogs and Whiz Kids. As you can probably guess, Easy Peasy are the easiest, Clever Clogs the next most difficult and Whiz Kids the hardest. However, the easiest questions are always the ones where you know the answers!

Good luck.

Quiz 1

1 What weapon were Big Willie and Little Willie the first examples of?

2 What was the colour of the first postage stamp?

3 Which British king was famous for having six wives?

4 Who was the previous British prime minister before Tony Blair?

5 What does the VE in VE Day stand for?

6 Was Trafalgar a sea, land or air battle?

7 Who commanded the British forces at Trafalgar?

8 In which year did World War I end?

9 In what city did Princess Diana die after a car crash?

10 With what decade was the fashion designer Mary Quant associated?

Answers

1. Tanks 2. Black (the penny black) 3. Henry VIII 4. John Major 5. Victory in Europe 6. A sea battle 7. Lord Nelson 8. 1918 9. Paris 10. The 1960s

Quiz 2

1 Which Roman emperor fiddled whilst Rome burned?

2 What creature became extinct in 1680?

3 Which wife of King Henry VIII survived him?

4 When did the first person travel into space?

5 In what year did the Suez Canal open?

6 Which emperor did Brutus and Cassius kill in the Roman Senate?

7 Who was the first to reach the South Pole?

8 In what year did President Nixon resign?

9 Which country handed over Florida to the USA in 1819?

10 What were the nationality of kamikaze pilots in World War II?

Answers

9. Spain 10. Japanese

1. Nero 2. The dodo 3. Catherine Parr 4. 1961 5. 1869 6. Julius Caesar 7. Roald Amundsen 8. 1974

Quiz 3

1 Which nation provided reinforcements to the British at Waterloo?

2 Who was the first wife of King Henry VIII?

3 In which English county is the site of the Battle of Edgehill?

4 What type of weapon was a Brown Bess?

5 Which country was historically known as New France?

6 Which space shuttle exploded in flight, killing all crew members?

7 How many children were born to Queen Victoria?

8 Who was Labour Party leader before Tony Blair?

9 In which two countries did the ancient Maya culture exist?

10 Which royal house did both Edward I and Richard II belong to?

Answers

1. Prussia 2. Catherine of Aragon 3. Warwickshire 4. A type of musket or gun 5. Canada 6. Challenger
7. Seven 8. John Smith 9. Mexico and Guatemala 10. House of Plantagenet

Quiz 4

1 How many Catherines did King Henry VIII have as wives?

2 What killed King Harold of England?

3 What was unusual about the childhood of the twins who founded Rome?

4 Which American president resigned over a scandal known as Watergate?

5 What type of event was Woodstock?

6 In which decade did it occur?

7 Which king was alleged to have commanded the sea to retreat?

8 Was the Battle of Agincourt a land or sea battle?

9 Who was Queen Victoria's husband?

10 What frontier wall was built in AD 122?

Answers

1. Three 2. An arrow 3. They were brought up by wolves 4. Richard Nixon 5. A music festival 6. The 1960s 7 King Canute 8. A land battle 9. Prince Albert 10. Hadrian's Wal

238

Quiz 5

1 What event started with the assassination of Arch-Duke Franz Ferdinand?

2 What throne was he heir to?

3 What didn't the British government fund until 1833?

4 In which century was the first photograph taken?

5 What did Eire do in 1949?

6 In what year did James I become King: 1405, 1601 or 1720?

7 By what name is East Pakistan now known?

8 What empire did Genghis Khan found?

9 What decade saw the arrival of teddy boys and rock 'n' roll?

10 Who was president of France until 1969?

Answers

7. **Bangladesh** 8. **The Mongol Empire** 9. **The 1950s** 10. **Charles de Gaulle**

1. **World War I** 2. **The Austrian** 3. **Schools** 4. **The 19th century** 5. **Declare itself a republic** 6. **1601**

Quiz 6

1 What important document was signed at Runnymede in the 13th century?

2 What Indian tribe did Geronimo lead?

3 Who was assassinated in 1968 by James Earl Ray?

4 In which century did Marco Polo visit China?

5 What was the system of picture writing used in Ancient Egypt called?

6 What did the Hudson Bay Company, set up in 1680, trade in?

7. Who was the first prime minister of an independent India?

8 Of which country were the Sui, the Han and the Three Kingdoms ruling dynasties?

9 Who was the first Communist leader of the Soviet Union?

10 In which civil war were the battles of Bull Run and Gettysberg?

Answers

1. Magna Carta 2. The Apache 3. Martin Luther King 4. 13th century 5. Hieroglyphics 6. Furs 7. Nehru 8. China 9. Lenin 10. The American Civil War

Quiz 7

1 Who had ships known as longships?

2 Was the Battle of Britain fought on land, sea or in the air?

3 Which ex-prime minister of Britain has a wife called Norma?

4 Around the banks of which river did the Ancient Egyptian culture develop?

5 With what sort of vehicle is the term stealth associated?

6 How many women prime ministers has Britain had?

7 How many female presidents of the United States have there been?

8 In what year did World War II start?

9 Was a trireme a Roman warship, a Greek council of war or a Saxon drink?

10 Who lived in a monastery?

Answers

9. A Roman warship 10. Monks

1. Vikings 2. In the air 3. John Major 4. The Nile 5. Military aircraft 6. One 7. None 8. 1939

Quiz 8

Clever Clogs

1 Which outlaw was shot by his own gang in 1852?

2 Who was the first president of the United States?

3 What do the initials NATO stand for?

4 What did Britain, Eire and Denmark do in 1973?

5 Which city in Peru was the centre of the Inca empire?

6 What was destroyed by a volcanic eruption in AD 79?

7 With what culture do you associate Socrates and Theseus?

8 What happened approximately 24,000 years ago?

9 Which Lady ruled Britain for just nine days?

10 In what year was Nelson Mandela released from prison?

Answers

1. Jesse James 2. George Washington 3. North Atlantic Treaty Organization 4. Join the European Economic Community 5. Cuzco 6. The city of Pompeii 7. Ancient Greek 8. The Ice Age 9. Lady Jane Grey 10. 1990

Quiz 9

1 Who came to the throne when Queen Victoria died?

2 Who did Charlemagne become king of in AD 771: the Franks, Goths or Vandals?

3 On which island did Eric the Red establish the first Viking colony?

4 Did he do this in 775, 982 or 1048?

5 Who was nicknamed, "the Lady of the Lamp"?

6 In what war did she tend injured troops?

7 What famous building in India was completed in 1643?

8 In what year did Prince Charles and Princess Diana agree a divorce?

9 In what year was Pope John Paul II elected?

10 How many popes were there that year?

Answers

7. Taj Mahal 8. 1996 9. 1978 10. Three

1. Edward VII 2. The Franks 3. Greenland 4. 982 5. Florence Nightingale 6. The Crimean war

243

Quiz 10

Easy Peasy

1 What do the initials RAF stand for?

2 In what year was the Magna Carta signed: 1180, 1300, 1215 or 1403?

3 Name one of the three countries which boycotted the 1980 Moscow Olympics?

4 Who was United States president before Bill Clinton?

5 What were the Zero, the Me109 and the Spitfire?

6 What disaster hit London in 1666?

7 What was mead: a type of bread, an alcoholic drink, a simple hut?

8 Who was the younger daughter of Henry VIII?

9 In what decade was the first *Star Wars* film released?

10 What famous London church was founded by Edward in 1052?

Answers

1. Royal Air Force 2. 1215 3. Kenya, the United States and West Germany 4. George Bush 5. World War II fighter aircraft 6. The Great Fire 7. An alcoholic drink 8. Elizabeth 9. The 1970s 10. Westminster Abbey

Quiz 11

1 Which country was Menachem Begin leader of in the 1970s?

2 Who travelled to Central Africa to find Dr Livingstone?

3 What book was completed in 1086?

4 Which island in the South Pacific features 600 mysterious stone head statues?

5 In the War of American Independence, which country joined in on America's side in 1779?

6 Who was Henry VIII's only son?

7 And who was the son's mother?

8 Which Celtic queen led a revolt against the Romans?

9 What was made up of cohorts and legions?

10 With which decade are mini skirts and Carnaby Street associated?

COO-EEE, DR. LIVINGSTONE ARE YOU THERE!

Answers

1. Israel 2. Henry Stanley 3. The Domesday book 4. Easter Island 5. Spain 6. Edward VI 7. Jane Seymour 8. Boudicca 9. Roman armies 10. The 1960s

245

Quiz 12

1   Who was the only American president to serve three consecutive terms in office?

2   Which Russian and British leaders was he joined by at the post-war Yalta conference?

3   Who was the first king or queen to be from the House of Windsor?

4   Robert Mugabe became leader of which African country in 1980?

5   What famous newspaper was published for the first time in 1785?

6   Which party was formed by Anton Drexler in 1919?

7   What happened to Rome in AD 455?

8   Which French monarch was known as the Sun King?

9   What depicted the Battle of Hastings in 72 scenes?

10 Who was defeated at Orleans in 1429 by an English army?

Answers

1. Franklin Delano Roosevelt 2. Stalin and Churchill 3. George V 4. Zimbabwe 5. *The Times* 6. The Nazi Party 7. It was destroyed 8. Louis XIV 9. The Bayeaux Tapestry 10. Joan of Arc

Quiz 13

True or false

1 The Incas also made mummies just like the Ancient Egyptians?

2 British television's Channel Four started broadcasting in 1991?

3 The Renaissance was a period of renewed interest in arts and learning starting in the 14th century?

4 1066–1400 is known as the Dark Ages?

5 The first farmers appeared around 10,000 years ago?

6 Which came first, the Stone Age or the Bronze Age?

7 Queen Elizabeth's Silver Jubilee was celebrated in 1979?

8 The V2 was a type of German submarine?

9 The first European ship to bring back slaves from West Africa was in 1441?

10 The Great Pyramid of Ancient Egypt was the tallest building in the world until the Eiffel Tower was built?

Answers

1. True 2. False 3. True 4. False 5. True 6. The Stone Age 7. False 8. False 9. True 10. True

247

Quiz 14

1 Which world leader dramatically resigned on New Year's Eve, 1999?

2 How many American colonies declared their independence in 1776: 4, 7 or 13?

3 Which English city was known to the Vikings as Jorvik?

4 What was the name of Nelson's flagship?

5 In both World War I and World War II, what was an "ace"?

6 Where did Roman senators meet to discuss matters of state?

7 In what century was the last civil war in Britain?

8 What financial event signalled the start of the Great Depression?

9 How many crusades were there?

10 Which two countries fought out the Hundred Years' War?

Answers

1. Boris Yeltsin 2. 13 3. York 4. HMS *Victory* 5. A fighter pilot who had shot down many enemy aircraft 6. The Senate 7. The 17th century 8. The Wall Street Crash 9. Eight 10. England and France

248

Quiz 15

Whiz Kids

1   In which World War I battle, lasting 141 days, did the British and French lose 600,000 men?

2   In what year was the last Viking attack on Britain: 980, 1066 or 1100?

3   What was abolished in the British Empire in 1833?

4   From what ship was the first SOS message broadcast?

5   In which year did Adolf Hitler become chancellor of Germany?

6   Which Italian family ruled Florence from the 15th century to the 18th century?

7   In which German town were the Nazi war leaders put on trial?

8   In what year was the Hubble Space Telescope launched?

9   What was the name of the Turkish empire which ruled from the 13th century until 1918?

10 What was the Praetorian Guard designed to protect?

Answers

1. The Somme 2. 1066 3. Slavery 4. The *Titanic* 5. 1933 6. The Medici family 7. Nuremberg 8. 1990 9. Ottoman Empire 10. Rome and its emperor

Quiz 16

1 What type of shop first opened in Britain in 1948?

2 What country was once ruled by shoguns?

3 In what decade did the Gulf War occur?

4 In 1980 which former actor became president of the United States?

5 How many atom bombs have been dropped?

6 What country did the Germans first invade to start World War II?

7 What was the nickname given to Baron von Richthofen in World War I?

8 Who crossed the Alps with elephants to attack Rome?

9 What sort of weapons are Scuds and Exocets?

10 Who explored parts of the Americas in 1492?

PERHAPS THIS WASN'T SUCH A GOOD IDEA!

Answers

1. A supermarket 2. Japan 3. The 1990s 4. Ronald Reagan 5. Two 6. Poland 7. The Red Baron 8. Hannibal 9. Missiles 10. Christopher Columbus

Quiz 17

1 Which country did Iraq invade to trigger off the Gulf War?

2 Who was the leader of Iraq at the time?

3 What famous castle held Allied prisoners in World War II?

4 Which Scottish king defeated the English at Bannockburn?

5 Western Europe had NATO, what was Eastern Europe's military alliance called?

6 What is the name for the Roman pictures made out of large numbers of small painted tiles?

7 William I started the construction of which London building in 1078?

8 What was the family surname of Henry VII?

9 What was the nickname of King Ivan of Russia?

10 What was discovered in California in 1848, starting a "rush"?

Answers

7. Tower of London 8. Tudor 9. Ivan the Terrible 10. Gold

1. Kuwait 2. Saddam Hussein 3. Colditz 4. Robert the Bruce 5. Warsaw Pact 6. Mosaics

Quiz 18

1 In which World War II battle did over 100,000 German troops surrender to the Russians?

2 Who was executed in front of Whitehall Palace in 1649?

3 What strange tax was abolished in Britain in 1851?

4 When were the last hangings in Britain?

5 What name was given to the medieval contest featuring two knights on horseback each with a lance?

DID I WIN?

6 Which "Great" leader created a vast empire from Greece to India in the period 336–323 BC?

7 What famous monument was sold by auction in 1915 for £6,600?

8 Which Indian prime minister was assassinated by her own bodyguards in 1986?

9 How large was the army that defeated the Saxons at the Battle of Hastings: 1,200, 5,000, 9,000 or 22,000?

10 Which European country was unified in 1861?

Answers

1. Stalingrad 2. King Charles I 3. Tax on windows 4. 1964 5. Jousting 6. Alexander the Great 7. Stonehenge 8. Indira Gandhi 9. 9,000 10. Italy

Quiz 19

1　Who was prime minister directly before John Major?

2　Where did Christopher Columbus land in 1498?

3　Who flies in Air Force One?

4　What were Sherman and Panzer examples of in World War II?

5　In which century did the French Revolution occur?

6　What in Roman times had a hot room, a warm room and a cold room?

7　In what civil war were the battles of Marston Moor and Naseby?

8　What new British political party formed in 1981?

9　Which American president was shot dead in a theatre in 1865?

10　Which country did Britain fight over rights to the Falkland Islands?

Answers

6. Roman baths　7. The English Civil War　8. The SDP　9. Abraham Lincoln　10. Argentina
1. Margaret Thatcher　2. Mainland America　3. The United States president　4. Tanks　5. The 18th century

Quiz 20

Clever Clogs

1 Who led the Afrika Korps in World War II?

2 What was his nickname?

3 Which British leader became famous for his rousing wartime speeches?

4 In what year were the Munich Olympics held?

5 Which German first started European printing with type?

6 Whose tomb was opened to much acclaim in 1922?

7 Who was the leader of the archaeological expedition to the above site?

8 Who sailed in the *Mayflower*?

9 What was the Black Death?

10 In which century did it occur?

Answers

1. General Rommel 2. The Desert Fox 3. Winston Churchill 4. 1968 5. Johannes Gutenberg 6. Tutankhamun 7. Howard Carter 8. The Pilgrim Fathers 9. Bubonic plague that swept Europe 10. 14th century

Whiz Kids

1   Who sailed in the *Beagle*?

2   How many years did Deng Xiaopeng rule China for?

3   Who became Lord Protector of England in 1653?

4   What was the name given to the North's forces in the American Civil War?

5   What was the largest amphitheatre in Roman times?

6   Was its capacity: 3,000, 11,000, 20,000 or 50,000?

7   At which London Underground station did 31 people lose their lives in 1987?

8   What did Queen Victoria celebrate in 1887?

9   Why did the ancient Chinese bury jade objects with the dead?

10 What name was given to the South's forces in the American Civil War?

Answers

7. King's Cross 8. Her golden jubilee (50 years as Queen) 9. They believed jade protected and preserved the dead body 10. Confederate

1. Charles Darwin 2. Twenty 3. Oliver Cromwell 4. Union 5. The Colosseum 6. 50,000

Quiz 22

1 What does the VJ in VJ Day stand for?

2 What were the Lancaster, the Heinkel He-III and the Liberator all examples of

3 How did Joan of Arc die?

4 Who led the Gunpowder Plot?

5 What caused the *Titanic* to sink in 1912?

6 Which monarch reigned longest in Britain?

7 What was the name of the airships which bombed London in 1915?

8 On which Japanese city was the first atom bomb dropped?

9 Who built Ermine Street and Fosse Way?

10 In what year did Japan bomb Pearl Harbor?

Answers

1. Victory in Japan 2. World War II bomber aircraft 3. She was burned at the stake 4. Guy Fawkes 5. Hitting an iceberg 6. Queen Victoria 7. Zeppelins 8. Hiroshima 9. The Romans 10. 1941

Quiz 23

1   What was the name given to the German's sustained bombing campaign of London and other British cities during World War II?

2   What two royal houses fought the War of the Roses?

3   Which ship was sunk at the Battle of the River Plate?

4   Who did Mary Tudor marry whilst Queen of England?

5   In the English Civil War, what was the name given to the anti-royalist forces?

6   Who was king of England immediately before Henry VIII?

7   Who did William of Normandy defeat at the Battle of Hastings?

8   Which general led the North's forces in the American Civil War?

9   How many times was Harold Wilson elected prime minister?

10 In what year was there a General Strike in Britain: 1906, 1916, 1926 or 1936?

Answers

1. The Blitz 2. York and Lancaster 3. *Graf Spee* 4. King Philip II of Spain 5. The roundheads 6. King Henry VII 7. King Harold 8. Ulysses S. Grant 9. Two 10. 1926

Quiz 24

1. In what year was the Panama Canal officially opened: 1876, 1906 or 1914?

2. Who was the last Russian tsar?

3. What happened to him and his family in 1917?

4. Who made the famous Gettysberg address in 1863?

5. Which famous pop star was shot dead in New York in 1980?

6. What house of kings followed the Tudors?

7. What country offered Albert Einstein its presidency in 1948?

8. Which country did Nikita Khrushchev lead in the 1950s?

9. What sports did the Scots government ban in 1467?

10. Which military leader was born in Corsica in 1769 and became Emperor of France in 1804?

Answers

1. 1914 2. Nikolaus II 3. They were executed 4. Abraham Lincoln 5. John Lennon 6. The House of Stuarts 7. Israel 8. The Soviet Union 9. Football and golf 10. Napoleon

Quiz 25

1   What Ancient Egyptian sculpture is the largest ancient world monument still in existence?

2   Gary Kasparov lost a famous chess contest in 1997; name the winner?

3   How many British general elections were there in 1974?

4   What material, beginning with P, did the Ancient Egyptians write on?

ROLL ON THE TYPEWRITER!

5   What was the name given to the people who wrote in Ancient Egyptian times?

6   Which wife of Henry VIII gave birth to Mary Tudor?

7   How many years was Henry married to this lady: 2, 4, 8 or 24?

8   With which continent is the explorer Robert Falcon Scott associated?

9   Which historic city is a holy place for three different religions: Mecca, Jerusalem or Baghdad?

10 What happened to the explorers Francis Drake, Captain James Cook and David Livingstone on their journeys?

Answers

1. The Sphinx 2. Deep Blue – a computer 3. Two 4. Papyrus 5. Scribes 6. Catherine of Aragon 7. 24 8. Antarctica 9. Jerusalem (Christian, Muslim and Jewish) 10. They all died whilst exploring

259

Quiz 26

1 What name was given to the Spanish fleet which set sail to invade England in 1588?

2 Who ruled England at the time?

3 Who was president of the United States during World War I?

4 King Alfred the Great defended large parts of Britain from invasion by whom?

5 Who became the first woman Speaker of the House of Commons in 1992?

6 Who was "Monty" of the Desert Rats?

7 Which aircraft carrier was sunk off the coast of Gibraltar in 1941?

8 What did Caligula, Augustus and Titus all have in common?

9 What royal house followed the House of Stuart?

10 The last execution of a witch in England took place in which year: 980, 1406 or 1712?

Answers

1. The Spanish Armada 2. Queen Elizabeth I 3. Woodrow Wilson 4. Vikings 5. Betty Boothroyd 6. Field Marshall Montgomery 7. HMS Ark Royal 8. They were all Roman emperors 9. Hanover 10. 1712

Quiz 27

1   In 1936, a march protesting about unemployment set off from which northern town?

2   Which famous Indian leader was known as The Mahatma, meaning Great Soul?

3   What scrolls were discovered in caves in Jordan in 1947?

4   Which South American country did Pizarro conquer in 1533?

5   Of which political party was Benjamin Disraeli the leader of during the Victorian era?

6   Which religion was directly influenced by the prophet, Muhammad, in the AD 600s?

7   What religion was introduced into Japan in 552?

8   What type of machine were the R101 and the Hindenberg, both built in the 1930s?

9   What revolt did Wat Tyler lead in 1381?

10 Which two Bolshevik leaders seized power in Russia in 1917?

Answers

1. Jarrow 2. Gandhi 3. The Dead Sea Scrolls 4. Peru 5. The Tory party 6. Islam 7. Buddhism 8. Passenger airships 9. The Peasants' Revolt 10. Lenin and Trotsky

Quiz 28

1 Members and supporters of CND marched in 1958, but what does CND stand for?

2 At the end of which war was the United Nations formed?

3 What year were the first free elections in South Africa?

4 Mao Zedong led the Communists to power in which country?

5 In what year was he made president of that country: 1936, 1949 or 1964?

6 Was General Patton: British, German, American or Italian?

7 What country did Cleopatra rule?

8 Which Asian war took place between 1965 and 1973?

9 What did the suffragettes campaign for?

10 Which famous army leader was known as the Iron Duke?

Answers

1. Campaign for Nuclear Disarmament 2. World War II 3. 1994 4. China 5. 1949 6. American 7. Ancient Egypt 8. The Vietnam war 9. Votes for women 10. Duke of Wellington

Quiz 29

1 Which American president was assassinated in 1963?

2 Who replaced him as the United States leader?

3 What language was spoken by the Ancient Romans?

4 Which African country did Italy invade in 1935?

5 What was a hoplite: a Greek foot soldier, a Saxon battleaxe or a sacred Norman drinking vessel?

6 Which leader described an "iron curtain" descending across Europe?

7 What event was recorded as first taking place in 776 BC at Olympia?

8 What country was known as Gaul in Roman times?

9 The first college of which university was established in 1249?

10 Which feared FBI chief died in 1972 after serving eight presidents?

Answers

1. John F. Kennedy 2. Lyndon Johnson 3. Latin 4. Abyssinia 5. A Greek foot soldier
6. Winston Churchill 7. The Olympic Games 8. France 9. Oxford University 10. J. Edgar Hoover

Quiz 30

1 Who was the leader responsible for Cambodia's "killing fields" of the 1970s?

2 What were a cross-staff and astrolabe used for?

3 Which king started the Hundred Years' War with France?

4 Who completed the first known round-the-world voyage?

5 From which country did he come from?

6 And in which century did he achieve the feat?

7 What was the name of Columbus's main ship when he first crossed the Atlantic?

8 Which country in the British Empire mutinied in 1857?

9 In which modern day country did the Assyrians live: Israel, Turkey, Morocco or Iraq?

10 Ssu Tsung was the last emperor of which Chinese dynasty?

Answers

1. Pol Pot 2. Navigation 3. Edward III 4. Ferdinand Magellan 5. Portugal 6. The 16th century 7. *Santa Maria* 8. India 9. Iraq 10. Ming

Quiz 31

1 Which two countries fought the Battle of Agincourt?

2 What word is used to describe the murder of six million Jews in the period 1933–45?

3 What was the name of the German air force in World War II?

4 In which culture was Zeus considered the king of the gods?

5 What was Romulus Augustulus the last of?

6 Egbert was the first British king to be converted to what?

7 What was a guillotine?

8 In which revolution was it first used?

9 Idi Amin was the dictator of which African country?

10 Which notorious Australian robber was hanged at Melbourne in 1880?

Answers

1. France and England 2. The Holocaust 3. Luftwaffe 4. The Ancient Greeks 5. Roman emperors 6. Christianity 7. A device for beheading people 8. The French Revolution 9. Uganda 10. Ned Kelly

Quiz 32

1 In 1637, Japan banned all foreigners apart from one country; which one?

2 In which decade was the Korean war fought?

3 What day did June 4, 1944, become known as?

4 Who shot John F. Kennedy and then was shot dead himself days later?

5 Belgium declared itself independent in 1831, but from which country?

6 What year was Britain given a 99 year lease on Hong Kong?

7 Which side used a Trojan Horse to enter the city of Troy?

8 Germany and Japan were two of the main Axis powers in World War II; can you name another?

9 What was Valhalla to the Vikings?

10 What nickname was given to Mary Tudor, Queen of England between 1583 and 1588?

Answers

1. The Netherlands 2. The 1950s 3. D-Day – the start of the Normandy Landings 4. Lee Harvey Oswald 5. The Netherlands 6. 1898 7. The Greeks 8. Italy (also Bulgaria and Romania) 9. The hall of the gods, where warriors who died in battle went 10. Bloody Mary

QUIZ 33

1 Who was Emperor of Japan during World War II?

2 The first passenger railway opened in 1825 between which two English towns?

3 Who was commander in chief of the Southern forces in the American Civil War?

4 Over the ownership of which two states did the US and Mexico fight in 1846–48?

5 What was the word, meaning lightning war, used to describe the Germans tactics as they swept across Europe during World War II?

6 Who was the first prime minister of England?

7 What was the system of racial segregation in South Africa called?

8 How many Conservative prime ministers of Britain have there been since 1950?

9 Who was the last British king to die in battle?

10 What deadly weapon was first used at the Battle of Ypres in 1915?

Answers

1. Hirohito 2. Stockton and Darlington 3. General Robert E. Lee 4. Texas and California 5. Blitzkrieg 6. Sir Robert Walpole 7. Apartheid 8. Seven 9. Richard III 10. Chlorine gas

Quiz 34

NICE OF DEM TO REMEMBER!

HAPPY VALENTINE

1 Which American political party did President Jimmy Carter represent: Republican or Democrat?

2 Which vegetable is Sir Walter Raleigh believed to have brought back from the Americas?

3 Which countries did Captain James Cook explore on his first long distance voyage?

4 Who was the Liberal Party leader before Charles Kennedy?

5 Who was the famous gangster responsible for the St Valentine's Day Massacre?

6 What was a blunderbuss: a methodist preacher, a type of gun or an early steam locomotive?

7 With which terrorist group is the political party, Sinn Fein, linked?

8 Pudding Lane in London was the starting point for which disaster in the 17th century?

9 In which decade was the first test tube baby born?

10 Offa's Dyke was built in England in the 8th century AD to keep out the people of which country?

Answers

1. Democrat 2. The potato 3. Australia and New Zealand 4. Paddy Ashdown 5. Al Capone 6. A type of gun 7. The IRA 8. The Great Fire of London 9. The 1970s 10. The Welsh

Quiz 35

1 Which country joined World War I in April 1917?

2 Which king was the first to become head of the Church of England?

3 Who was the first Labour prime minister?

4 The Gunpowder Plot was an attempt to assassinate whom?

5 The Treaty of Versailles was signed after which war?

6 Which king of England was forced by the country's barons to sign the Magna Carta?

7 Whose forces were defeated at the battle of Actium?

8 In what year was Dachau, the first Nazi concentration camp for Jews, established?

9 In 1979, which country was invaded by Soviet troops?

10 Which famous explorer died in poverty in 1506?

Answers

1. The United States 2. Henry VIII 3. James Ramsey MacDonald 4. King James I 5. World War I 6. King John 7. Cleopatra and Mark Antony 8. 1933 9. Afghanistan 10. Christopher Columbus

Quiz 36

1　Which island people killed Captain Cook in 1779?

2　What did the Luddites protest against?

3　The Gunpowder Plot led by Guy Fawkes rolled 36 barrels of explosives underneath which building?

4　What did the term SALT stand for in the 1970s and 1980s?

5　What happened to the boat *Rainbow Warrior* in 1985?

6　Who owned the boat?

7　On which island was Napoleon exiled for the last six years of his life?

8　What do the initials PLO stand for?

9　What opened between Paddington and Farringdon Street in 1863?

10　What was cosmonaut Aleksei Leonov the first to do?

Answers

1. The Hawaiian islanders 2. The factory conditions and machinery of the Industrial Revolution
3. The Houses of Parliament 4. Strategic Arms Limitation Talks 5. It was blown up by the French secret
service 6. Greenpeace 7. St Helena 8. Palestine Liberation Organization 9. The world's first
underground railway 10. Walk in space

Quiz 37

1 Benito Mussolini ruled which European country in the 20th century?

2 Did his rule end in the 1930s, 1940s or 1970s?

3 Which country did Russia sell Alaska to?

4 The potato famine struck which country in the period 1845–46?

5 Live Aid was a charity concert in aid of which famine-stricken African country: Rwanda, Ethiopia or Morocco?

6 Was Live Aid held in 1978, 1985, 1990 or 1992?

7 King George VI was the father of which well-known member of the British royal family?

8 King James I had which famous explorer executed: Sir Francis Drake, Sir Walter Raleigh or Sir Francis Chichester?

9 What sort of weapon did China first test in the 1970s?

10 Did the Ancient Greeks, Egyptians or Romans build the Sphinx?

Answers

1. Italy 2. 1940s 3. The United States 4. Ireland 5. Ethiopia 6. 1985 7. Queen Elizabeth II 8. Sir Walter Raleigh 9. Nuclear bomb 10. Ancient Egyptians

Science & Maths

Here are 37 quizzes to see what you know about science and mathematics. Included are questions on astronomy, computers, scientists and their inventions.

The quizzes are divided into three levels of difficulty: Easy Peasy, Clever Clogs and Whiz Kids. As you can probably guess, Easy Peasy are the easiest, Clever Clogs the next most difficult and Whiz Kids the hardest. However, the easiest questions are always the ones where you know the answers!

Good luck.

Quiz 1

1 What does a thermometer measure?

2 What is a *Triceratops* an example of?

3 What precious metal and element has the atomic symbol Ag?

4 What is a half plus an eighth?

5 Which planet is nearest to the Sun?

6 What did Orville and Wilbur Wright successfully build?

7 What planet did the two Viking spacecraft land on?

8 What is 50% of 122?

9 How many sides does a triangle have?

10 Which British and French plane is the only supersonic airliner in service?

Easy Peasy

Answers

1. Temperature 2. A dinosaur 3. Silver 4. Five-eighths 5. Mercury 6. The first heavier-than-air aircraft 7. Mars 8. 61 9. Three 10. Concorde

Quiz 2

1 What is the longest side of a triangle called?

2 What scientific device did Dutch spectacle-maker Hans Lippershey invent?

3 How much is 35% of 300?

4 At what temperature in centigrade does water boil?

5 What type of triangle has three sides of equal length?

6 Which British engineer is associated with the invention of the jet engine?

7 What element has the chemical symbol Fe?

8 How do you write 1.5 as a vulgar fraction?

9 What happens to an object if it accelerates?

10 What can you tell from the rings of a tree trunk?

Answers

1. The hypotenuse 2. The telescope 3. 105 4. 100 degrees 5. An equilateral triangle 6. Sir Frank Whittle 7. Iron 8. 1½ 9. Its speed increases 10. The age of the tree

1. What famous table did Russian, Dmitri Mendelev produce?

2. What number did an Indian by the name of Vyas invent in the 7th century AD?

3. What computer input device was invented by Douglas Englebart?

4. What did astronomer William Herschel discover?

5. What does Vitamin D help keep strong and healthy?

6. What important computer component was invented in 1970/71?

7. What takes 247.7 years to orbit the Sun?

8. What geological era lasted for 135 million years and is commonly called the age of the reptiles?

9. Was the Jurassic period part of the above era?

10. How many stars are estimated to be in the Milky Way: 20 billion, 200 million or 200 billion?

Answers

1. The periodic table of elements 2. Zero 3. The mouse 4. Uranus 5. Bones and teeth 6. The microprocessor 7. Pluto 8. Mesozoic 9. Yes 10. 200 billion

Quiz 4

1 How many grammes in a kilogram?

2 Does hot air travel up or down?

3 What element has the chemical symbol O?

4 What does the North pole of a magnet do?

5 How many threes are in 39?

6 Which planet is known as the red planet?

7 How many sides has a pentagon?

8 Where would you find a femur bone?

9 Which raw material is most plastic made from?

10 What is 100 divided by four?

Answers

1. 1,000 2. Up 3. Oxygen 4. Point to Magnetic North 5. 13 6. Mars 7. Five 8. In your leg 9. Oil 10. 25

Quiz 5

1   Which Ancient Greek had a theorem about triangles?

2   What are COBOL, FORTRAN and LISP examples of?

3   Who invented the lightning conductor?

4   Which vitamin helps fight disease and helps seeing in the dark?

5   What part of a car can come in disc and drum form?

6   What electronic device was first developed in 1948 by Walter Brattain and others?

7   Which planet has 12 satellites or moons?

8   Who developed his General Theory of Relativity?

9   How many bits in a byte?

10 What was NASA's *Columbia* the first example of?

QUIET PLEASE
EXPERIMENT
IN
PROGRESS

Answers

1. Pythagoras 2. Computer languages 3. Benjamin Franklin 4. Vitamin A 5. Brakes 6. The transistor 7. Jupiter 8. Albert Einstein 9. Eight 10 The space shuttle

Quiz 6

1 There are three elements which can be magnetised. Iron is one — name the other two?

2 What is the more common name for sodium chloride?

3 Which Danish astronomer had a nose made out of silver and wax?

4 What machine first worked for a living in 1961?

5 Did Puma, Unimation or AEG make the machine in question 4?

6 How many degrees do the angles in a pentagon add up to?

7 What is the average human body temperature?

8 How many hours are there in a week?

9 What part of an atom did Ernest Rutherford discover in 1919?

10 What does the scientific abbreviation r.p.m. stand for?

Answers

1. Nickel and Cobalt 2. Table salt 3. Tycho Brahe 4. Robot 5. Unimation 6. 540° 7. 37°C 8. 168 9. Proton 10. Revolutions per minute

Quiz 7

1 What covers more than two thirds of the world's surface?

2 At room temperature, is helium a gas, a liquid or a solid?

3 How many degrees do the angles of a triangle add up to?

4 What fruit fell on Sir Isaac Newton's head making him consider gravity?

5 What paper is used to measure acids and alkalis?

6 If the paper in question five is dipped in acid, what colour does it turn?

7 What were the Manchester Mark I and the Colossus early examples of?

8 What is the most common element in the Earth's atmosphere?

9 If you received four pounds pocket money a week, how many weeks would you have to save up to reach 36 pounds?

10 What name was given to the American missions to the Moon?

Answers

1. Water 2. A gas 3. 180 4. An apple 5. Litmus paper 6. Red 7. Computers 8. Nitrogen 9. Nine 10. Apollo

Quiz 8

Clever Clogs

1 What does a van der Graaf generator create?

2 What does the term AI stand for?

3 What is the base two number system more commonly known as?

4 Who invented the process for freezing food?

5 Can lightning strike in the same place twice?

6 What important gas did Joseph Priestley discover in 1774?

7 What type of boat has one or more sets of wings underwater which help lift much of the craft above the water?

8 What two metals is solder largely a mixture of?

9 How many sides does a rhombus have?

10 What does the Mohs scale measure?

Answers

1. Static electricity 2. Artificial Intelligence 3. Binary 4. Clarence Birdseye 5. Yes 6. Oxygen 7. Hydrofoil 8. Lead and tin 9. Four 10. Hardness of a material

Quiz 9

Whiz Kids

1 What word describes the path travelled by a body in space?

2 What do you do if you boot up a computer?

3 What is an oxide?

4 How is a black hole created?

5 What synthetic fibre was invented by American chemist Wallace Carothers?

6 What part of the body secretes the hormone insulin?

7 Is the element mercury: a solid, a liquid or a gas at room temperature?

8 If a material is said to be ductile, what can be done to it?

9 What is desalination?

10 What is dilute acetic acid better known as?

NO, THAT ISN'T HOW YOU *BOOT* UP A COMPUTER, CARL.

Answers

1. Orbit 2. Start it 3. A compound of oxygen and another element 4. By a massive star collapsing in on itself 5. Nylon 6. The pancreas 7. A liquid 8. It can be drawn into thin wires 9. Producing fresh water by removing salt from sea water 10. Vinegar

Quiz 10

Easy Peasy

1 What type of engine are a turboshaft and a turbofan examples of?

2 How many centimetres in nine metres?

3 What name do we give to a portable store of electrical energy, sometimes known as a cell?

4 How many sides do quadrilaterals have?

5 What metal are most soft drinks cans made of?

6 What is the lightest element of all: helium, hydrogen or fluorine?

7 How long is a year on Saturn: 9, 79 or 29 Earth-years?

8 Who invented dynamite and gave his name to a famous series of prizes?

9 What does a pneumatic drill use to provide it with power?

10 What piece of computing equipment can come in the forms dot matrix, laser and inkjet?

Answers

1. Jet engine 2. 900 3. Battery 4. Four 5. Aluminium 6. Hydrogen 7. 29 8. Alfred Nobel 9. Air 10. Printer

Quiz 11

Clever Clogs

1　In base two numbers, what do you get by adding 11 and 1?

2　What first example of this device filled a hall 140 square metres and weighed 30 tonnes?

3　What does Halley's Comet do every 76 years?

4　Who performed the first ever heart transplant operation?

5　What does a Geiger counter measure?

6　Does sound travel faster through air or water?

7　What are the three states of matter?

8　What name is given to people who break into a computer system without permission?

9　What insect transmits the disease malaria?

10　What makes Dolly the sheep so special?

Answers

1. 100　2. Computer　3. Completes its orbit around the Sun　4. Dr Christiaan Barnard　5. Radioactivity　6. Through water　7. Solid, liquid and gas　8. Hackers　9. The mosquito　10. It was the first mammal to be cloned from another adult mammal!

Quiz 12

1 What is the hardest naturally occurring substance?

2 Does a star implode or explode to become a black hole?

3 What does the computer term RAM stand for?

4 Which American inventor counts the electric light and sound recording amongst his inventions?

5 What is an ore?

6 Which important metal can be obtained from the ores hematite and magnetite?

7 Who was the first woman in space?

8 What is the unit of electrical current called?

9 What is calcium carbonate commonly known as?

10 What device did Elisha Otis invent in 1853?

Answers

1. Diamond 2. Implode 3. Random Access Memory 4. Thomas Alva Edison 5. A mineral from which metals can be obtained 6. Iron 7. Valentina Tereshkova 8. The ampere (or amp) 9. Chalk 10. The lift or elevator

Easy Peasy

1 Which number is bigger – a: 8 x 7 or b: 63 – 8?

2 Which planet is the largest in our solar system?

3 How many sides has a hexagon?

4 What arithmetical aid did Sir Clive Sinclair first sell in 1973?

5 What is a machine for burning large amounts of rubbish called?

6 Do magnets with different poles facing attract or repel?

7 What did Igor Sikorsky do in 1939?

8 What is 30% of 120?

9 What type of space instrument was named after Edwin Hubble?

10 How many sides does a snowflake have?

Answers

1. a (8 x 7 = 56 while 63–8 = 55) 2. Jupiter 3. Six 4. Electronic calculator 5. An incinerator 6. Attract 7. Build the world's first helicopter 8. 36 9. A telescope 10. Six

Quiz 14

True or false

1 Some museums already have robot security guards patrolling their floors?

2 The aircraft *Voyager* flew for nine days without refuelling to travel around the world?

3 The oldest known living person reached 149 years of age?

4 A fax page is made up of as many as six million individual dots?

5 If your body temperature reaches 30 degrees centigrade, you will fall unconscious?

6 You use over 200 muscles when you walk?

7 The gravity on Jupiter is 318 times stronger than on Earth?

8 There are canals on Mars?

9 Robodoc is a surgical assistant robot with over 1,000 successful operations under its belt?

10 1968 saw the launch of the first spacecraft?

Answers

1. True 2. True 3. False 4. True 5. True 6. True 7. True 8. False 9. True 10. False

Quiz 15

1 On which planet did the Pathfinder mission land in 1996?

2 What do the letters DC stand for in electricity?

3 What is measured in millibars?

4 What term is used to describe the amount of matter in an object?

5 What are the three primary colours of light?

6 If the base of a triangle is 3 cm and its height 4cm, what is its area?

7 In the base two number system what does 1011+10 equal?

8 Who hosted the long-running astronomy show *The Sky at Night*?

9 What term describes the change in shape or size of an object when a force is applied to squash or stretch it?

10 What element has the chemical symbol Na?

Answers

1. Mars 2. Direct Current 3. Atmospheric pressure 4. Mass 5. Red, blue and green 6. 6cm 7. 1101 8. Patrick Moore 9. Elasticity 10. Sodium

Quiz 16

1 Do magnets with the same poles facing each other repel or attract?

2 What is white spirit made from: petroleum, plant fibres or diluted mercury?

3 What type of power station splits atoms to create electricity?

4 Is a kilogram more or less than two pounds?

5 Which planet is most famous for its rings?

6 What common device did Laszlo Biro of Argentina invent in 1944?

7 What is the second most common element in air?

8 Are all metals magnetic?

9 What body in our solar system is 330,000 times bigger than Earth and only a quarter as dense?

10 How much of a cake is left if you eat 4/8 of it?

Answers

1. Repel 2. Petroleum 3. A nuclear power station 4. More 5. Saturn 6. The ballpoint pen 7. Oxygen 8. No, only three 9. The Sun 10. Half of it

Quiz 17

Clever Clogs

1 What does the abbreviation NASA stand for?

2 What is the length of the outer edge of a circle better known as?

3 What reflects heat better, black or white?

4 What is the ohm a measurement of?

5 Which planet is the closest in size to Earth?

6 What term describes the atoms of two or more elements bonded together by a chemical reaction?

7 Is an electron a positive or negatively charged particle of an atom?

8 Who was the first person in space?

9 What do the letters AC stand for in electricity?

10 Which planet did the space probe *Mariner 10* pass three times?

Answers

1. National American Space Administration 2. Circumference 3. White 4. Electrical resistance 5. Venus
6. Compound 7. Negatively charged 8. Yuri Gagarin 9. Alternating Current 10. Mercury

Quiz 18

1 What is another name for solid carbon dioxide?

2 Which female scientist won a Nobel prize for chemistry for her work investigating radioactivity?

3 What element is present in every organic compound?

4 What were *Skylab* and *Salut* early examples of?

5 What is the glowing piece of wire in a light bulb called?

6 What metal is the wire in question four commonly made from?

7 What is the force of flight which moves an aircraft forward?

8 What is the force of flight which pulls an aircraft back?

9 What is a catalyst in chemistry?

10 How much space in megabytes does a standard 3.5 inch floppy disk contain?

Answers

1. Dry ice 2. Marie Curie 3. Carbon 4. Space stations 5. The filament 6. Tungsten 7. Thrust 8. Drag 9. A substance that changes the rate of a chemical reaction 10. 1.44 megabytes

Quiz 19

1 With what sort of power are the engineers James Watt and Thomas Newcomen associated?

2 What part of a computer is sometimes called a VDU?

3 Is the radius of a circle bigger or smaller than the circle's diameter?

4 In what industry would you find a rig, tankers and a refinery?

5 What is the symbol for the chemical element Nitrogen?

6 As a fraction, how much is 25% of something?

7 How much more hydrogen than oxygen would you find in water?

8 What happened in space on July 20, 1969?

9 What is the solid form of water called?

10 How many poles does a permanent magnet have?

Answers

1. Steam 2. A monitor or computer screen 3. Smaller (the radius is half the diameter) 4. The oil industry 5. N 6. ¹/₄ 7. Twice as much 8. People reached the Moon 9. Ice 10. Two

Quiz 20

1 What is the second largest planet in the solar system?

2 Is there any air on the Moon?

3 In what year did the first space shuttle fly?

4 What mineral rates one on the Mohs scale?

5 Carbohydrates contain three elements; carbon and oxygen are two, what is the third?

6 What is an alloy?

7 John Logie Baird is associated with the invention of what machine?

8 What is the term maglev short for?

9 What is the term used to describe when a substance changes from a liquid to a gas?

10 Does a convex surface bend inwards or outwards?

Answers

7. Television 8. Magnetic levitation 9. Boiling point 10. Outwards
1. Saturn 2. No 3. 1981 4. Talc 5. Hydrogen 6. A substance composed of two or more metals

Quiz 21

Whiz Kids

1 Is the boiling point of silver higher than iron?

2 What is the name of the hole in your eye which lets light in?

3 In physics, what is the name given to a rod which turns around a fixed point?

4 What is the value of pi?

5 What uses about 40% of all silver?

6 What was the name of the rocket which propelled the Apollo missions to the moon?

7 What is a compact flash card?

8 What force of flight is generated by an aircraft's wings?

9 What types of energy does a light bulb give off?

10 Who invented the electric dynamo in 1831?

Answers

1. No. Iron's boiling point is higher 2. The pupil 3. A lever 4. 3.142 5. Camera film 6. Saturn V 7. A portable form of computer memory storage 8. Lift 9. Heat and light energy 10. Michael Faraday

Quiz 22

Easy Peasy

1 What is the name given to magnets powered by electricity?

2 When water becomes ice, does it expand or contract?

3 How many times does 9 go into 81?

4 What was the name of the first man on the Moon?

5 What was the name of the spacecraft which took him there?

6 What metal is a good conductor of heat and electricity and is used in plumbing and wiring?

7 What clothing device did Whitcomb Judson invent in 1892?

8 Did the United States, China or the USSR send the first satellite into space?

9 What was the name of the satellite in question eight?

10 What part of a car engine sets fire to the petrol and air mixture in a cylinder?

Answers

1 What invention of James Martin made the lives of military jet pilots much safer?

2 What is the branch of science that studies metals called?

3 George Stephenson invented what form of transport?

4 Who was the second man on the Moon?

5 What medical instrument is used to listen to the sounds within the body?

6 How long was the first aircraft flight: five minutes, 12 seconds or 11 minutes?

7 What are the names of the bones that make up the spine called?

8 What two elements make up sand?

9 What does ISP mean in computing?

10 Who invented the first car driven by an internal combustion engine?

YES, I CAN DEFINITELY HEAR PUMPING SOUNDS.

Answers

1. The ejection seat 2. Metallurgy 3. The steam locomotive 4. Edwin "Buzz" Aldrin 5. Stethoscope 6. 12 seconds 7. Vertebrae 8. Oxygen and silicon 9. Internet Service Provider 10. Karl Benz

Quiz 24

Whiz Kids

1 Celsius and Farenheit are two temperature scales; can you name another one?

2 In which country was the magnetic compass invented?

3 A polymer is a substance made of a chain of small molecules; what are these small molecules called?

4 If a material has the property of malleability what does it mean?

5 Who invented the spinning jenny?

6 What is a vacuum?

7 Can light travel through a vacuum?

8 Deoxyribonucleic acid is better known by three capital letters; what are they?

9 Who discovered the structure of the substance in question eight?

10 Which is the lightest metal: lithium, titanium or silver?

Answers

1. Kelvin 2. China 3. Monomers 4. It can be hammered and shaped into thin sheets 5. James Hargreaves 6. A space which is empty of air and any other molecules 7. Yes 8. DNA 9. Watson and Crick 10. Lithium

Quiz 25

1 How many planets are there in our solar system?

2 Which is the least dense state of matter?

3 What sort of vehicle did Sir Christopher Cockerell invent?

4 If you rub a balloon against a woolly sweater, what do you help generate?

5 What is the chemical symbol of the metal aluminium?

6 When water reaches its boiling point, what does it become?

7 How many weeks are there in five years?

8 If two angles of a triangle add up to 140 degrees, what must the third angle be?

9 What navigational device uses a magnet suspended or floated in a liquid?

10 Did plesiosaurs live in water, in the air or on land?

Answers

1. Nine 2. Gas 3. The hovercraft 4. Static electricity 5. Al 6. Steam (water vapour) 7. 260
8. 40 degrees 9. A magnetic compass 10. In water

Quiz 26

Clever Clogs

1 Which planet did William Herschel discover in 1781?

2 Is a single year on this planet equal to four, 24 or 82 Earth-years?

3 What harmful substance is produced by burning fossil fuels and is a major cause of acid rain?

4 What is the corrosion of iron and steel commonly known as?

5 What two metals make the alloy bronze?

6 What does the diameter of a circle multiplied by pi equal?

7 What is the meaning of the initial, CAD?

8 What word, beginning with D, is the study of forces and motion?

9 What was the first spacecraft with more than one crew member: *Gemini 1*, *Mercury 4* or *Voskhod 1*?

10 What is 0.125 as a fraction?

Answers

298

7. Computer Aided Design 8. Dynamics 9. *Voskhod 1* 10. ¹/₈ (one-eighth)
1. Uranus 2. 82 3. Sulphur dioxide 4. Rust 5. Copper and tin 6. The circumference of the circle

Quiz 27

Whiz Kids

1. What name is given to a triangle with three different length sides?

2. What acid is found in the sting of an ant?

3. What radioactive element was discovered by the German, Martin Klaproth, in 1841?

4. What term, beginning with B, is the chemical opposite to acids?

5. What is kaolin an alternative name for?

6. What is the only letter not to appear anywhere on the periodic table of elements?

7. How long does it take for light from the Sun to travel to Earth?

8. What is the name of the space station which will be in service from 2004?

9. Are the noble gases very reactive or unreactive?

10. What colour flame is produced when a substance containing potassium is burned?

Answers

1. Scalene 2. Formic acid 3. Uranium 4. Base 5. China clay 6. J 7. Five minutes 8. International Space Station 9. Unreactive 10. Purple

299

Quiz 28

1 Was the dinosaur *Brontosaurus* a meat or plant eater?

2 How many days are there in seven weeks?

3 What sort of vehicle were the *Stratocruiser*, the *HP42* and the *Vickers Viscount*?

4 Were they powered by jet or piston engines?

5 What is the chemical symbol for lead?

6 Is a palmtop computer larger or smaller than a notebook computer?

7 If three angles in a quadrilateral equal 300 degrees, what is the size of the fourth angle?

8 What are the three solar system planets farthest away from the sun?

9 What does a vacuum flask do to liquids?

10 What is the centre of an atom called?

NO, NO... BRING ME SOMETHING I CAN EAT!

Answers

1. Plant eater 2. 49 3. Airliners 4. Piston engines 5. Pb 6. Smaller 7. 60 degrees 8. Uranus, Neptune and Pluto 9. Keeps them hot or cool 10. The nucleus

Quiz 29

1   Which is heavier, 10 kilograms or 22 pounds?

2   In chemistry, what is centrifuging used for?

3   What is 240 volts in Britain and 110 volts in some other countries?

4   Is sound a form of energy?

5   Approximately how many grams would you find in an ounce?

6   What is 32 degrees fahrenheit equal to in centigrade?

7   How many planets in the solar system have a greater surface gravity than Earth?

8   What colour flame does burning a substance containing calcium produce?

9   What name is given to a triangle with two equal length sides?

10 What computer peripheral would you use to transfer pages of text and pictures onto your computer?

Answers

1. 10 kilograms 2. To separate out solid particles from a liquid 3. The household electricity supply
4. Yes 5. 28 6. Zero 7. Two, Jupiter and Neptune 8. Red 9. Isosceles 10. Scanner

Quiz 30

1 What does the term OCR stand for?

2 Who was the first woman to walk in space?

3 What device did Robert Watson-Watt invent in 1935?

4 What are the three things needed for combustion to occur?

5 What unit is equal to a thousand million bytes?

6 What is pharmacology the study of?

7 What important material is made with the help of a Bessemer converter?

8 What does carbon dioxide do to limewater?

9 A human being has 24, 30 or 46 chromosomes?

10 What did John Boyd Dunlop invent in 1888?

Answers

1. Optical Character Recognition 2. Svetlana Savitskaya 3. Radar 4. Heat, fuel and oxygen 5. A gigabyte 6. Drugs 7. Steel 8. Turn it milky 9. 46 10. Pneumatic tyres

Quiz 31

1 What is measured using pH numbers?

2 What type of energy does a photovoltaic cell convert into electricity?

3 What colour flame is produced when a substance containing copper is burned?

4 Where would you find the patella bone in your body?

5 What do the initials VR stand for?

6 What is the smallest number divisible by both 3 and 4?

7 With what communications device would you associate the name of Marconi?

8 What does the plastic covering around an electric wire do?

9 Which planet was the last to be discovered?

10 What is the name of the rod on a car which joins two wheels together?

Answers

1. Whether a substance is acid or alkali 2. Light energy 3. Bluish green 4. Kneecap 5. Virtual reality 6. 12 7. Radio 8. Insulates the wire and protects people when handling it 9. Pluto 10. The axle

Quiz 32

1   What kind of light gives people suntans?

2   Yellow, orange, red and green are four colours of the spectrum; can you name the other three?

3   What was the *Bell XI* the first craft to do?

4   Who piloted the *Bell XI* on its historic flight?

5   What machine is used to move a fluid?

6   What space probe, named after a famous astronomer, travelled to Jupiter and four of its moons?

7   How many minutes are there in a day?

8   Name the only other supersonic airliner to fly other than Concorde?

9   What is the main ingredient used in making glass?

10 If a substance tests as neutral, what number would it be given on the pH scale?

Answers

1. Ultraviolet light 2. Blue, violet and indigo 3. Travel faster than the speed of sound 4. Chuck Yeager 5. A pump 6. *Galileo* 7. 1,440 8. Tupolev Tu-144 9. Sand 10. Seven

1 Which comet orbits the Sun every 76 years?

2 What is an LED?

3 What kind of camera was invented by Edwin Land?

4 What are A, B, AB and O the four types of in humans?

5 What is the chemical symbol of Zinc?

6 What is the boiling point of water in fahrenheit?

7 In computing, what do the initials CPU stand for?

8 What is another name for the base ten number system?

9 Which element comes in a number of forms including graphite?

10 In the base two number system, what is 10011 + 101?

Answers

6. 212 degrees 7. Central Processing Unit 8. Decimal 9. Carbon 10. 11000

1. Halley's Comet 2. Light-emitting diode 3. The Polaroid instant camera 4. Blood groups 5. Zn

Quiz 34

Easy Peasy

1 The Montgolfier Brothers were the first to build what sort of flying machine?

2 A tin can is made of a thin layer of tin over steel, copper or bronze?

3 What sort of machines were *Saturn V* and *Ariane 4*?

4 How many sevens are there in 28?

5 How many sides does a parallelogram have?

6 What sort of code uses just dots and dashes to spell out words?

7 What temperature measuring device did famous astronomer Galileo invent?

8 What nationality was Galileo?

9 How many twenty pence chocolate bars could you buy with four pounds?

10 The study of shapes and angles is called algebra, calculus or geometry?

Answers

1. Hot air balloon 2. Steel 3. Space rockets 4. Four 5. Four 6. Morse code 7. Thermometer 8. Italian 9. 20 10. Geometry

Quiz 35

1 What device, with the full name modulator-demodulator, is used to connect your computer to the Internet?

2 What term describes the Moon coming between the Sun and the Earth, covering the Sun up from our view?

3 In computing, what do the initials ROM stand for?

4 What machine can vary its density to travel underwater or on the water's surface?

5 What is a magneto?

6 What was sent across the Atlantic for the first time in 1901?

7 What gemstone was first produced artificially in 1955?

8 Which pair flew the Atlantic for the first time in 1919?

9 What does antifreeze do to water's freezing point?

10 What broadcast radio waveband operates from 160–255 kHz?

Answers

1. Modem 2. An eclipse 3. Read-Only Memory 4. A submarine or submersible 5. A simple form of electricity generator 6. Radio signals 7. Diamond 8. Alcock and Brown 9. It lowers it 10. Long wave

Quiz 36

1 What was the name of the first space probe to send back pictures of Venus?

2 What vitamin, found in liver and green vegetables, helps with clotting blood?

3 What substance's chemical name is calcium oxide?

4 What household cleaning device was invented by Cecil Booth in 1901?

5 Can you convert the base two number 101 into base ten?

6 What is estimated to have occurred over 15,000 million years ago?

7 How big is one nanometre?

8 What does an ammeter measure?

9 What is an antiseptic?

10 What is geothermal energy?

Answers

1. Venera 9 2. Vitamin K 3. Lime 4. Vacuum cleaner 5. Five 6. The Big Bang 7. One billionth of a metre 8. Electric current 9. A substance which kills or prevents the growth of germs 10. Energy using volcanic heat from beneath the ground

Easy Peasy

1 What type of machine are the *EH101*, the *Sea King* and the *Chinook*?

2 What part of a personal computer acts as a permanent store of the user's files and programs?

3 What important fuel and raw material is measured in barrels?

4 What did Louis Blériot cross in his aircraft in 1909?

5 How many sides does a heptagon have?

6 To split an atom is called fusion or fission?

7 What do wind turbines produce at a wind farm?

8 Which is the second smallest planet in the solar system?

9 When clothes dry outside, what process, beginning with E, causes the water to disappear?

10 When molecules are heated do they move faster or slower?

Answers

8. Mercury 9. Evaporation 10. Faster

1. Helicopters 2. The hard disk 3. Oil 4. The English Channel 5. Seven 6. Fission 7. Electricity

Notes

Notes

Notes